Handbook
of
Oscilloscopes

Theory
and
Application

John D. Lenk
Consulting Technical Writer

PRENTICE-HALL, INC.
Englewood Cliffs, N.J.

PRENTICE-HALL SERIES IN ELECTRONIC TECHNOLOGY

Dr. Irving L. Kosow, editor

Charles M. Thomson and Joseph J. Gershon, consulting editors

PRENTICE-HALL INTERNATIONAL, INC., *London*
PRENTICE-HALL OF AUSTRALIA, PTY. LTD., *Sydney*
PRENTICE-HALL OF CANADA, LTD., *Toronto*
PRENTICE-HALL OF INDIA PRIVATE LTD., *New Delhi*
PRENTICE-HALL OF JAPAN, INC., *Tokyo*

Library of Congress Catalog Card Number: 68–20858
Printed in the United States of America

*Dedicated to my wife Irene
and daughter Karen*

Preface

The manufacturers of oscilloscopes provide elaborate instruction manuals on the operation and circuit theory of their particular instruments. Rarely, however, do these manuals give any *applications data* describing the many uses of oscilloscopes. Even the training films and service courses of the largest and best-known oscilloscope manufacturers are notably lacking in such material. For example, how do you use an oscilloscope to find the switching time of a diode, or the hysteresis and saturation factor of a computer memory core?

The *Handbook of Oscilloscopes* fills the gap in information; it can be used to supplement the operating instructions of any oscilloscope, whether it be a low-cost shop type, or a precision laboratory instrument.

A variety of test procedures using the oscilloscope as the basic tool are described in "cookbook" fashion. Each procedure is preceded by a brief description of the "why" and "where" for the particular test. These descriptions offer a digest to readers who may be unfamiliar with some specialized oscilloscope applications and want to put the step-by-step procedures to immediate use. Each operation is illustrated with test connection diagrams and typical oscilloscope waveforms. Although every known use of an oscilloscope has not been included, those practical, experience-proven applications are here.

Assuming that some readers are not familiar with the operating principles and characteristics of oscilloscopes, the initial chapters give *simplified* presentations of these details. Chapters 1–4 cover oscilloscope basics—typical operating controls, specifications, and performance—as well as a brief description of oscilloscope accessories. Throughout, the descriptions are kept to the block diagram or simplified schematic level. Unnecessary and elaborate circuit descriptions are avoided.

The book thus serves the dual purpose of a basic textbook for student technicians or beginners and a factual guidebook for experienced, working technicians.

The author has received much help from various organizations in writing this book. He wishes to give special thanks to the following: Allied Radio, Hewlett-Packard, Sencore, and Tektronix, Inc., General Electric, Motorola, Texas Instruments, Society of Motion Picture and Television Engineers.

J.D.L.

Contents

10 CHECKING AMPLIFIERS AND AMPLIFIER CIRCUITS 145

11 CHECKING COMMUNICATIONS EQUIPMENT 160

CHAPTER 1

Oscilloscope Basics

The cathode-ray oscilloscope (CRO) is an extremely fast X-Y plotter capable of plotting an input signal versus another signal, or versus time, whichever is required. A luminous spot acts as a "stylus" and moves over the display area in response to input voltages. In most applications, the Y axis (vertical) input receives its signal from the voltage being examined, moving the spot up or down in accordance with the instantaneous value of the voltage. The X axis (horizontal) input is usually an internally generated linear ramp voltage which moves the spot uniformly from left to right across the display screen. The spot then traces a curve which shows how the input voltage varies as a function of time.

If the signal under examination is repetitive, at a fast enough rate, the display appears to stand still. The CRO is thus a means of visualizing time-varying voltages. As such, the oscilloscope has become a universal tool in all kinds of electronic investigations. Oscilloscopes operate on voltages. It is possible, however, to convert current, strain, acceleration, pressure, and other physical quantities into voltages by means of transducers, and thus to present visual representations of a wide variety of dynamic phenomena on oscilloscopes.

The formal name *cathode ray oscilloscope* is usually abbreviated to *oscilloscope* or, simply, *scope*. An *oscillograph* is the pictorial representation of an oscilloscope trace. Some older texts apply the word "oscillograph" to the complete equipment.

1-1. The Cathode-ray Tube

All circuits of an oscilloscope are built around a cathode-ray tube (CRT). Figure 1-1 shows the internal construction of a typical tube of this type. As with other vacuum tubes, the filament heats the cathode to the degree where it emits electrons. The control grid influences the amount of current flow, as in standard vacuum tubes. Two anodes are used, each having a positive d-c potential applied to it. These anodes accelerate the electrons and form them into a beam. The intensity of the beam is regulated by the potential applied to the control grid.

The cathode consists of a nickel cylinder with an emitting element fused at its end. This element is made of either barium or strontium oxide and permits a release of sufficient electrons for an electron stream to form.

The grid structure, although controlling electron flow as in conventional tubes, differs from the wire mesh of receiving tubes and consists of a cylinder with a tiny circular opening, to keep the electron stream small enough. The beam is focused into a sharp pinpoint by controlling the voltage on the first anode. The two anodes of the cathode-ray tube can be compared to a glass lens system, such as used in movie projectors, because the anodes focus the beam to a pinpoint at the face of the tube. A high voltage is applied to the

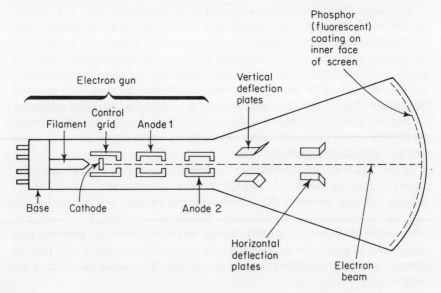

Fig. 1-1. Internal construction of CRT used in CROs.

second anode so that the electron stream will attain high velocity for increased intensity and visibility when it strikes the tube face. The beam-forming section of the tube is known as an *electron gun*.

The inside of the tube face is coated with phosphor so that, when electrons strike this coating, it will *fluoresce* and emit light. After the exciting electron stream has left the area, the fluorescing characteristics which emit light rapidly decay, and the light level is reduced. The chemical composition of the coating, however, can be such that the emitted light persists for an appreciable interval, so that one can observe the light visually. Since the beam is swept across the tube at a fairly rapid rate during normal operation, the light must persist for a time interval sufficient for it to leave a complete trace of the waveform drawn on the tube face. At the same time, the persistence of the phosphorescent coating should be sufficiently short so that, if the beam stops, the pattern traced on the tube will disappear very rapidly.

A standard numbering system is used, within the tube designation code, for ready identification of the phosphor characteristics. For example, if 3AP1 is a cathode-ray tube's numerical designation, the tube has a 3-in. face, because the first number identifies the face diameter. The P1 designation indicates a medium persistence phosphor, which has a green glow when excited. The A designation refers to the internal construction and indicates that this particular tube has some structural changes with respect to a 3P1 cathode-ray tube.

1-2. Beam Deflection System

As shown in Fig. 1-1, two sets of plates are present within the tube, beyond the second anode. These plates are for deflecting the electron beam both horizontally and vertically so that the beam will "write out" information delivered to the deflecting system. Such a system is known as *electrostatic deflection* and is predominantly used in oscilloscopes. Magnetic deflection, once used in a few oscilloscopes, is more often used in TV picture tubes and radar displays.

The electrostatic beam deflection is accomplished through the two pairs of parallel plates. For example, a voltage applied across the horizontal deflection plates will influence the beam, because the negative potential on one of the horizontal plates repels the electron stream, whereas the positive potential on the other horizontal deflection plate attracts the beam. If such a voltage is a sawtooth type, the gradually rising potential of the sawtooth will gradually pull the beam toward the positive horizontal deflection plate. Therefore, the electron beam is made to scan across the face of the tube. Also, any potential applied to the vertical deflection plates will cause the beam to move vertically.

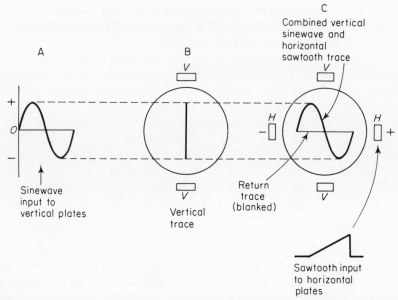

Fig. 1-2. Vertical sine wave and horizontal sawtooth sweep produce CRO trace.

Figure 1-2 shows how an oscilloscope traces out a sine wave on the tube face, when such a signal is applied to the vertical input of the oscilloscope. In Fig. 1-2(a), the sine wave applied at the vertical input of the oscilloscope is shown. If the internal horizontal sweep generator is turned off, the rising positive potential of the first alternation of the input signal causes the electron beam to move upward, as shown in Fig. 1-2(b). When the negative alternation of the input signal arrives at the vertical deflection plates, the electron beam is pulled downward from the center, also as shown in Fig. 1-2. The rapid rise and fall of the signal alternation causes the electron beam to move up and down the face of the cathode-ray tube very rapidly, leaving a vertical line trace.

If the horizontal oscillator within the oscilloscope is now turned on, a sawtooth of voltage, as shown in Fig. 1-2(c), will be applied to the horizontal deflection plates. The rising potential of the sawtooth voltage causes the right horizontal plate to become positive and the left horizontal plate to become negative. The negative left plate and the positive right plate cause the beam to move from left to right, because the beam is repelled by the negative plate and attracted by the positive plate. If one sawtooth occurs for each cycle of the sine wave signal, the beam will be pulled across the face of the tube once for each cycle. Thus, as the first alternation of the input cycle rises in amplitude, the electron beam would normally rise in a vertical plane, as shown in Fig. 1-2(b). The sawtooth on the horizontal plates gradually pulls the beam from left to right and traces out the input signal waveshape in visual form.

1-3. Basic Frequency Measurement

Waveshapes of square waves, pulses, or any other types of signals can be observed on the face of the oscilloscope screen. If the input signal has a frequency twice that of the sawtooth applied to the horizontal plates, two cycles will appear on the screen, because the beam is pulled across the screen only once for each two cycles of the input signal. By regulating the ratio of the input signal frequency to the sawtooth sweep frequency, portions of the input signal, or a number of cycles of the input signal, can be made visible on the screen. By calibrating the frequency of the horizontal sweep waveform so that its exact frequency is known, the frequency of the input signals to the oscilloscope can be calculated. For example, if four cycles of a sine wave appear on the screen and the sawtooth generator is set for 100 cycles, the frequency of the signal applied at the input of the oscilloscope is 400 cycles.

1-4. Basic Voltage Measurement

In addition to frequency measurements, the oscilloscope can be used for reading the peak-to-peak voltages of a-c signals, pulses, square waves, etc., as well as d-c voltages. For reading voltages, a transparent plastic screen is attached to the face of the oscilloscope. Such a screen (also known as *grid, grid mask, mask, grating, graticule*) is found in several forms. Usually, a screen is a transparent scale with vertical and horizontal lines spaced one division apart. The screen is fitted against the screen of the CRT. This allows time and amplitude to be read directly. These graduated scales often have small markings which subdivide the major divisions to assist in making accurate measurements. Most laboratory oscilloscopes are set up in centimenters. Some shop oscilloscopes are calibrated in inches. Still other oscilloscopes use no particular standard of measurement, but are simply equal-spaced "divisions." *In all the procedures throughout this book it is assumed that the oscilloscope is calibrated in centimeters.*

To calibrate the oscilloscope screen, an a-c voltmeter of known accuracy is used initially. A low-voltage a-c signal must be present for calibration. Some oscilloscopes have a terminal on the front panel which supplies such an a-c reference voltage. For example, if the reference voltage is 5 volts, this voltage is applied to the vertical input terminal of the oscilloscope. The internal horizontal sweep generator is shut off so that a vertical trace, as shown in Fig. 1-2(b), is visible on the screen. This vertical line represents the peak-to-peak voltage of the input signal. The vertical height control is then adjusted so that the line is five divisions high, and the control is left in this position after calibration. Knowing the RMS value of the applied a-c calibrating voltage, the peak-to-peak voltage can be calculated by multiplying the RMS value by 1.41 to obtain the peak value, then doubling the peak value to obtain the peak-to-peak value.

1-5. Basic Oscilloscope Circuits

Figure 1-3 is a block diagram of a *typical* oscilloscope. It would be almost impossible, and beyond the scope of this book, to describe all the circuits in modern oscilloscopes. Many of these circuits are special purpose. The basic circuits are used in various combinations. Instead of attempting a description of every circuit and combination, the following discussion covers a *complete* working oscilloscope.

1-5-1. Vertical (Y-Axis) Channel

Signals to be examined are usually applied to the vertical, or *Y*, deflection plates through the vertical amplifier. A vertical deflection amplifier is required, since the signals are usually not strong enough to produce measurable vertical deflection on the CRT. A typical CRT requires 50 volts dc to produce a deflection of 1 in. The high-gain amplifier in a laboratory type of oscilloscope permits a 1-in. deflection with 0.5 millivolt; the average shop type of oscilloscope requires at least 20 millivolts for a 1-in. deflection. Another difference between laboratory and shop amplifiers is the frequency response. As in the case of any amplifier, the frequency response must be wide enough to pass faithfully the *entire band* of frequencies to be measured on the oscilloscope. For simple audio work, an upper limit of 200 kHz is sufficient. TV service requires a passband of at least 5 MHz. Some laboratory oscilloscopes provide up to 1000 MHz (1 GHz); 50 MHz is common for laboratory scopes.

When high-voltage signals are to be examined, they can be applied directly to the vertical deflection plates on most oscilloscopes.

The vertical amplifier output is also applied to the sync amplifier through the sync selector switch in the internal position. This permits the horizontal sweep circuit to be triggered by the signal being examined.

1-5-2. Horizontal (X-Axis) Channel

Usually the horizontal deflection plates are fed a sweep voltage that provides a time base. As in the case of the vertical channel, the horizontal plates are fed through an amplifier, but they can be fed directly when the voltages are of sufficient amplitude. When external signals are to be applied

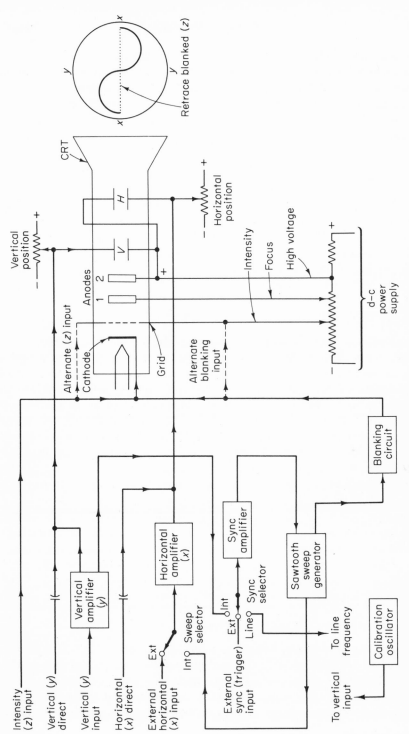

Fig. 1-3. Simplified block diagram of typical oscilloscope.

7

to the horizontal channel, they can also be fed through the horizontal amplifier, via the sweep selector switch in the external position. When the sweep selector is in the internal position, the horizontal amplifier receives an input from the sawtooth sweep generator which is triggered by the sync amplifier.

In most oscilloscopes, the sawtooth sweep voltage is generated by a multivibrator, relaxation oscillator, or pulse generator. There are four basic types of sweeps. The *recurrent* sweep presents the display repetitively, and the eye sees a lasting pattern. In a *single sweep*, the spot is swept once across the screen in response to a trigger signal. The trigger can be obtained from the signal under study, or from an external source. In most cases, a *driven sweep* is used where the sweep is recurrent but triggered by the signal under test. In special cases, some oscilloscopes provide a *nonsawtooth sweep*, such as a sine wave.

Sweep frequencies vary with the type of oscilloscope. A laboratory oscilloscope may have sweep frequencies up to several megahertz; a simple shop oscilloscope for audio work has an upper limit of 100 kHz. Most TV service requires a horizontal sweep frequency up to 1 MHz.

Whatever type of sweep is used, it must be synchronized with the signal being investigated. If not, the pattern will appear to drift across the screen in a random fashion. Hence a sync system is needed. Three usual sources for synchronization can be selected by the sync selector: internal, where the trigger is obtained from the signal under investigation (through the vertical amplifier); external, where an external trigger source is also used to trigger or initiate the signal being measured; and line, where the sync trigger is obtained from the line frequency. Line sync is often used in TV service where an external sweep generator and an oscilloscope are both triggered at the line frequency.

The oscilloscope sweep system is also used to produce a *blanking* signal. The blanking signal is necessary to eliminate the retrace that would occur when the sweep trace snaps back from its final (right-hand) position to the initial or starting point. This retrace could cause confusion if it were not eliminated by blanking the CRT during the retrace period with a high negative voltage on the control grid (or a high positive voltage on the CRT cathode). The blanking voltage is usually developed (or triggered) by the sweep generator.

1-5-3. Intensity (Z-Axis) Channel

Intensity modulation, sometimes known as *Z-axis modulation*, is accomplished by inserting a signal between ground and the cathode (or control grid) of the CRT. When the signal voltage is large enough it can cut off the CRT on selected parts of the trace, just as the retrace blanking signal does. Z-axis modulation is applied during the normally visible portion of the trace.

The Z-axis can also be used to brighten the trace. Periodically applying positive pulse voltages to the CRT control grid (or negative pulses to the cathode) brightens the electron beam throughout its trace to give a third, or Z, dimension. These periodically brightened spots can be used as markers for time calibration of the main waveform.

1-5-4. Positioning Controls

For many measurements, it is necessary to provide some means of positioning the trace on the CRT face. Such centering provisions are accomplished by applying small, independent, internal d-c potentials to the deflection plates and controlling them by means of potentiometers. The centering or positioning controls are particularly useful during voltage calibration, and during enlargement of a waveform for examination of small characteristics. The portion of interest may move off the CRT screen so that positioning controls are necessary to bring it back on again.

1-5-5. Focus and Intensity Controls

The CRT electron beam is focused in a manner similar to that of an optical lens, but the focal length is altered by changing the ratio of potentials between the first and second anodes. This ratio is changed by varying the potential on the anode with the focus control, which is a potentiometer usually located on the oscilloscope front panel. The potential on the second anode remains constant.

The intensity of the beam is varied by the intensity control potentiometer which changes the grid potential with respect to the cathode, thus permitting more or fewer electrons to flow. Because the potentials applied to the control grid and to both anodes are taken from a common voltage divider network, any change made in the setting of the intensity control requires a compensating change in the setting of the focus control, and vice versa.

1-5-6. Calibration Circuit

Most laboratory oscilloscopes have an internally generated and stabilized waveform of known amplitude which serves as a calibrating reference. Usually, a square wave is used, with the calibrating signal accessible on a front panel connector.

On shop oscilloscopes, the 60 Hz line voltage is used. Either way, the calibrating voltage can be applied to the vertical channel by running a lead between the front panel calibration output connector and the vertical input connector. On some oscilloscopes, the calibrating voltage is applied to the vertical input through a front panel control switch.

1-5-7. Other Oscilloscope Circuits

Those familiar with oscilloscope circuits will note that the discussion has not covered many basic controls, such as amplifier gain or attenuation, astigmatism, sweep frequency, time, sync polarity, trigger level, slope, to name a few. These controls, as well as all other controls of typical oscilloscopes, are covered from the operator's viewpoint in the following chapter.

CHAPTER 2

Basic
Operating Controls

This chapter deals with the operating controls of oscilloscopes. Because of the large variety of oscilloscopes it is impossible to discuss the controls of each make and model. As stated in the Preface, the functions of oscilloscope operating controls usually are fully covered in the related instruction manuals. Therefore, it is operating controls for typical oscilloscopes that are briefly described here.

All oscilloscopes have some operating controls in common. For example, most oscilloscopes have controls which position the trace vertically and horizontally. Not all controls, however, are found in any one oscilloscope. A simple, inexpensive oscilloscope will not have a single sweep control or operating mode where a single sweep can be displayed. Controls and connectors are not always found in the same location and in the same form on all oscilloscopes. On one instrument, the astigmatism control is a front-panel operating knob; on another, a side-panel screwdriver adjustment fills the same function.

Figures 2-1 and 2-2 show the front-panel operating controls of two representative oscilloscopes. As will be seen, both units have some controls in common (with the same, or different, names), but each oscilloscope has certain unique controls.

The control functions for each oscilloscope described are presented in the following sections.

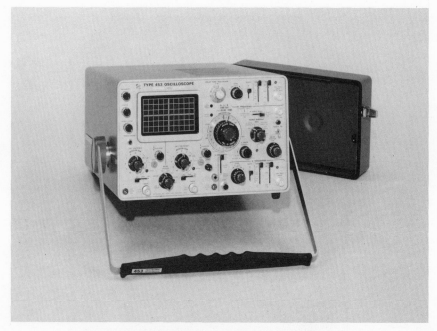

Fig. 2-1. Tektronix type 453 oscilloscope.

2-1. Tektronix Type 453 Oscilloscope

The Tektronix Type 453 Oscilloscope is a transistorized portable oscilloscope designed to operate in a wide range of environmental conditions. (See Fig. 2-1.) The dual-channel d-c to 50 MHz vertical system provides calibrated deflection factors from 5 millivolts to 10 volts/division. Channels 1 and 2 can be cascaded using an external cable to provide 1 millivolt minimum deflection factor. The trigger circuits provide stable triggering over the full range of vertical frequency response. The horizontal sweep provides a maximum sweep rate of 0.1 microsecond/division (10 nanoseconds/ division, using 10 × magnifier) along with a delayed sweep feature for accurate relative-time measurements. Accurate X-Y measurements can be made with Channel 2 providing the vertical deflection and Channel 1 providing the horizontal deflection.

The following paragraphs describe the function or operation of the controls and connectors, together with comments on how these controls relate to similar controls on other oscilloscopes.

INTENSITY. Controls brightness of the display. The display can be adjusted from very bright to total darkness. The setting of the intensity control may affect the correct focus of the display. Slight readjustment of the focus control may be necessary when the intensity level is changed.

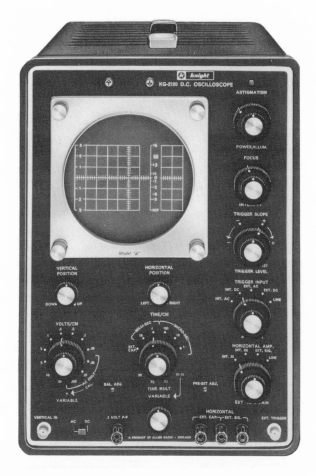

Fig. 2-2. Knight KG-2100 d-c oscilloscope.

To protect the CRT phosphor of any oscilloscope, do not turn the intensity control higher than necessary to provide a satisfactory display. Also, be careful that the intensity control is not set too high when changing from a fast to a slow sweep rate.

FOCUS. Provides adjustment for a well-defined display. If a well-defined trace cannot be obtained with the focus control, it may be necessary to adjust the astigmatism control. To check for proper setting of the astigmatism adjustment, slowly turn the focus control through the optimum setting. If the astigmatism adjustment is correctly set, the vertical and horizontal portions of the trace will come into sharpest focus at the same position of the focus control. This setting of the astigmatism adjustment should be correct for any display. It may, however, be necessary to reset the focus control slightly when the intensity control is changed.

SCALE ILLUM. Controls graticule illumination. The engraved lines of the transparent viewing screen are brightened by edge-lighting the graticule. This provides a sharp reproduction of the lines when photographs are made from the screen, but does not produce an interfering glare.

TRACE FINDER. Returns the display to the screen, when pressed, by reducing horizontal and vertical deflection. The trace finder provides a means of locating a display which overscans the viewing area either vertically or horizontally. This type of control is found only in a precision laboratory oscilloscope.

VOLTS/DIV. Selects vertical deflection factor. The amount of vertical deflection produced by a signal is determined by the signal amplitude, the attenuation factor of the probe (if used), the setting of the volts/div switch, and the setting of the variable volts/div control. The calibrated deflection factors indicated by the volts/div switches apply only when the variable control is set to the cal position. On some shop-type oscilloscopes, this control (called *V-gain (amplitude) control* or *Y-gain (amplitude) control*) is a variable potentiometer rather than a step-attenuator. On other oscilloscopes, the combination step-attenuator and variable control are used. In that case, the potentiometer provides continuously variable control of vertical gain in any one of the ranges provided by the step-attenuator. In some shop-type oscilloscopes, the step-attenuator portion is calibrated as a multiplier (such as $\times 0.1$, $\times 1.0$, $\times 10.0$, $\times 100.0$, $\times 1000.0$) rather than in specific values of volts per division.

VARIABLE. Provides continuously variable deflection factor to at least 2.5 times setting of volts/div switch.

POSITION (vertical). Controls vertical position of trace. This control (also called *vertical position control* or *Y-position control*) moves the trace up and down to any desired vertical position on the screen.

GAIN. Screwdriver adjustment to set gain of the vertical preamplifier. This is usually an internal adjustment control on most oscilloscopes.

AC GND DC. Selects method of coupling input signal to grid of input amplifier (vertical).

AC: D-c component of input signal is blocked (by coupling capacitor inserted between vertical input connector and amplifier).

GND: Input circuit is grounded (does not ground applied signal).

DC: All components of the input signal are passed to the input amplifier.

STEP ATTEN BAL. Screwdriver adjustment to balance input amplifier in the 5-, 10-, and 20-mV positions of the volts/div switch. This control is usually an internal adjustment control on most oscilloscopes.

INPUT. Vertical input connector for signal.

MODE. Selects vertical mode of operation. This control (or similar control) is found only on oscilloscopes having more than one mode of operation.

CH 1: Channel 1 signal displayed.

CH 2: Channel 2 signal displayed.

Alt: Dual-trace display of signal on both channels; display switched at end of each sweep.

Chop: Dual-trace display of signal on both channels; approximately 1 microsecond segments from each channel displayed at a repetition rate of about 500 kHz.

Add: Channel 1 and 2 signals algebraically added and algebraic sum displayed on the CRT.

Trigger. Source of internal triggering signal selected from vertical system. This control is found only on oscilloscopes having an alternate trigger source.

Norm: Sweep circuits triggered from displayed channel or channels.

CH 1 Only: Sweep circuits triggered only from signal on Channel 1.

INVERT. When pulled out, inverts the vertical display. When observing certain signals (such as TV waveforms) the signal is often displayed upside down. The invert switch permits the display to be viewed right side up. On some oscilloscopes, the control (called a *trace reverser*) switch positions are labeled (+) for an upright pattern and (−) for an inverted display.

EXT TRIG INPUT. Input connector for external triggering signal. Connector in B triggering section of front panel also serves as external horizontal input when horiz display switch is in ext horiz position.

SOURCE. Selects source of triggering signal. This control (also called *sync selector*) selects the type of signal used to synchronize the horizontal sweep oscillator.

Int: For most applications, the sweep can be triggered internally. In the int position, the trigger signal is obtained from the vertical system.

Line: The line position of the source switch connects a sample of the power-line frequency to the trigger generator (and thus to the horizontal sweep oscillator). Line triggering is useful when the input signal is time-related to the line frequency. It is also useful for providing a stable display of a line-frequency component in a complex waveform.

Ext: An external signal connected to the ext trig input connector can be used to trigger the sweep in the ext position of the source switch. The external signal must be time-related to the displayed signal for a stable display. An external trigger signal can be used to provide a triggered display when the internal signal is too low in amplitude for correct triggering or contains signal components on which it is not desired to trigger. It is also useful when signal tracing in amplifiers, phase-shift networks, wave-shaping circuits, etc. The signal from a single point in the circuit can be connected to the ext trig input connector through a signal probe or cable. The sweep is then triggered by the same signal at all times and allows amplitude, time relationship, or waveshape changes of signals at various points in the circuit to be examined without resetting the triggering controls.

Ext ÷ 10: Operation in the ext ÷ 10 position is the same as described for ext, except that the external triggering signal is attenuated 10 times.

COUPLING. Determines method of coupling triggering signal to trigger circuit. On some oscilloscopes, this function is combined with the trigger source control.

AC: The a-c position blocks the d-c component of the trigger signal. Signals with low-frequency components below about 30 Hz will be attenuated. In general, a-c coupling can be used for most applications. If the trigger signal contains unwanted components, or if the sweep is to be triggered at a d-c level, one of the remaining coupling switch positions will provide a better display.

The triggering point in the a-c position depends on the *average* voltage level of the trigger signal. If the trigger signals occur in a random fashion, the average voltage level will vary, causing the triggering point to vary also. This shift of the triggering point may be enough to make it impossible to maintain a stable display. In such cases, use d-c coupling.

LF Rej: In the LF Rej position, d-c is rejected and signals below about 30 kHz are attenuated. Therefore, the sweep signals will be triggered only by the higher-frequency components of the signal. This position is particularly useful for providing stable triggering if the trigger signal contains line-frequency components.

HF Rej: The HF Rej position passes all low-frequency signals between about 30 Hz and 50 kHz. D-c is rejected and signals outside the given range are attenuated. When triggering from complex waveforms, this position is useful for providing stable display of low-frequency components.

DC: D-c coupling can be used to provide stable triggering with low-frequency signals which would be attenuated in the a-c position, or with low-repetition rate signals. The level control can be adjusted to provide triggering at the desired d-c level on the waveforms. When using internal triggering, the setting of the vertical position controls affects the d-c trigger level.

SLOPE. The triggering slope switch determines whether the trigger circuit responds on the positive-going or negative-going portion of the trigger signal. Shop-type oscilloscopes usually do not have a slope switch function. When the slope switch is in the (+) (positive-going) position, the display will start with the positive-going portion of the waveform; in the (−) (negative-going) position, the display will start with the negative-going portion of the waveform. (See Fig. 2-3.) When several cycles of a signal appear in the display, the setting of the slope switch is probably unimportant. If only a certain portion of a cycle is to be displayed, correct setting of the slope switch provides a display which starts on the desired slope of the input signal.

LEVEL. The triggering level control determines the voltage level on the triggering waveform at which the sweep is triggered. On shop-type oscil-

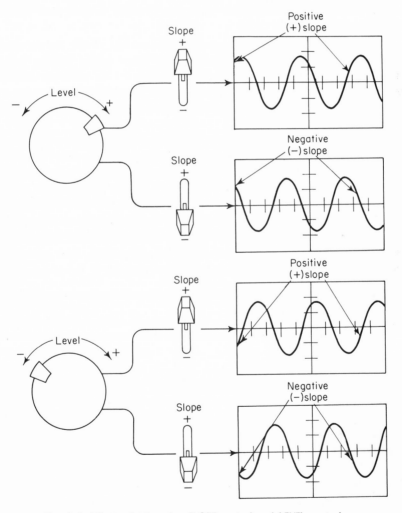

Fig. 2-3. Effects of triggering SLOPE control and LEVEL control.

loscopes, this control is usually called the *sync or trigger amplitude control*, and its adjustment varies the amplitude of the sync voltage applied to the internal horizontal sweep generator. The sawtooth sweep locks in with the sync voltage, and the display stands still when the level control is properly set. When the level control is set in the (+) region, the trigger circuit responds at a more positive point on the trigger signal. When the level control is set in the (−) region, the trigger circuit responds at a more negative point on the trigger signal. Figure 2-3 illustrates this effect with different settings of the slope switch.

A SWEEP MODE. Determines sweep operating mode of A section of the dual-trace. On shop-type oscilloscopes, this control is usually called the *sweep selector*, and provides three basic operating modes: linear sawtooth sweep (internal), external, and line-frequency sine wave (internal). On oscilloscopes designed specifically for television receiver service there are usually two special sweep frequencies: 30 Hz, the TV vertical deflection frequency and 7875 Hz, the TV horizontal deflection frequency.

Auto Trig. Automatic triggering can be used for most applications. It is particularly useful where a reference trace is needed in the absence of a trigger signal. When a trigger signal is available, a stable display can be obtained by correct adjustment of the level control. When the trigger repetition rate is less than about 20 Hz, or in the absence of a trigger signal, the sweep generator runs free to produce a reference trace. When a trigger signal is again applied, the free-running condition ends and the sweep generator is triggered to produce a stable display.

Norm Trig: Operation in the norm trig postion when a trigger signal is applied is the same as in the auto trig position. When a trigger signal is not applied, the sweep generator remains off and the screen is blanked. The norm trig mode is used to display signals with repetition rates below about 20 Hz, or when a trace is not desired in the absence of trigger signals.

Single Sweep: When the signal to be displayed is not repetitive or varies in amplitude, shape, or time, a conventional repetitive display may produce an unstable presentation. The single sweep mode is used to avoid this condition. The single sweep can also be used to photograph a non-repetitive signal.

TIME/DIV. The time/div switch selects calibrated horizontal sweep rates for the internal sweep generators. The variable control provides continuously variable sweep rates between the settings of the time/div switch. The calibrated sweep rates indicated by the time/div switch apply only when the variable control is set to the cal position. On some shop-type oscilloscopes, the time/div switch is called the *sweep range selector* or the *coarse frequency control*. In such instruments, the switch positions are calibrated in terms of frequency rather than time (typically 10–100 Hz, 100–1000 Hz, 1–10 kHz, and 10–100 kHz). In laboratory-type oscilloscopes, the sweep rates are expressed in time for convenience, since the time interval of the display is of greater importance than sweep frequency for most scientific measurements. If time were not given directly, it would have to be calculated from frequency, as is true of most shop-type oscilloscopes.

VARIABLE. Provides continuously variable sweep rate to at least 2.5 times setting of time/div switch. On shop-type oscilloscopes, this control is usually called the *sweep frequency control, fine frequency control,* or *frequency vernier,* and permits continuous variation of sweep frequency within any of the ranges provided by the sweep range selector.

SWEEP LENGTH. Adjusts length of the horizontal sweep. In the full position, the sweep is about 11 divisions long. As the control is rotated counterclockwise, the sweep length will be reduced until it is less than 4 divisions long just before the detent in the fully counterclockwise position is reached. On shop-type oscilloscopes, this control is usually called the *H-gain (amplitude) control* or *X-gain (amplitude) control.* On some oscilloscopes, a combination step-attenuator and variable control is used. In that case, the potentiometer provides continuously variable control of vertical gain in any one of the stages provided by the step-attenuator. Usually, the step-attenuator is calibrated as a multiplier (such as $\times$ 1.0, $\times$ 10.0, $\times$ 100.0).

POSITION (horizontal). Controls horizontal position of trace. This control (also called *horizontal centering control, horizontal position control,* or *X-position control*) moves the trace left and right to any desired horizontal position on the screen.

Z-AXIS INPUT. Input connector for intensity modulation of the CRT display. Intensity (Z-axis) modulation can be used to relate further information to the displayed signal without changing the shape of the waveform. The modulating signal is applied to the CRT through the Z-axis input binding posts. The voltage amplitude required for visible trace modulation depends on the setting of the intensity control. A Z-axis gain control is incorporated in many oscilloscopes. Adjustment of this control (also called *intensity modulation gain* or *amplitude control*) provides continuous variation of the intensity-modulation voltage. Time markers applied to the Z-axis input provide a direct time reference on the display. With uncalibrated horizontal sweep or external horizontal deflection, the time markers provide a means of reading time directly from the display. If the markers are not time-related to the display waveform, a single-sweep display should be used (internal sweep only) to provide a stable display. The sharpest display is provided by intensity modulation signals with a fast rise and fall.

1 KC CAL. Calibration signal output connector. The internal 1 kHz

square-wave calibrator provides a convenient signal source for checking vertical gain and basic horizontal timing. The calibrator provides peak-to-peak square-wave voltages of 0.1 and 1.0 volt. Voltage range is selected by the calibrator switch. The calibrator signal is very useful for checking and adjusting probe compensation. In addition, the calibrator can be used as a convenient signal source for application to external equipment. In shop-type oscilloscopes, the calibrating voltage is a line-frequency sine wave obtained from a filament winding of the oscilloscope power transformer and set to 1 volt (or 0.1 volt) peak-to-peak by means of a voltage divider. In some oscilloscopes, a calibration voltage control allows this voltage to be adjusted between zero and 1 volt peak-to-peak.

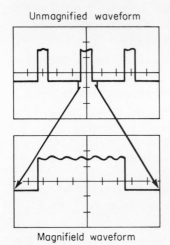

Unmagnified waveform

Magnifield waveform

Fig. 2-4. Operation of a sweep magnifier.

MAG. Increases sweep rate to 10 times setting of time/div switch by horizontally expanding the center division of the display. This permits closer observation of a part of the signal. As shown in Fig. 2-4, the center division of the unmagnified display is the portion visible on the screen in magnified form. Equivalent length of the magnified sweep is about 100 divisions. Any 10-division portion may be viewed by adjusting the horizontal position control to bring the desired portion into the viewing area. A sweep magnifier control is usually found only on laboratory-type oscilloscopes.

NOTE

The remaining controls for the Type 453 Oscilloscope as shown in Fig. 2-1 are unique to this oscilloscope, or to a similar laboratory instrument. Therefore, they are not discussed here.

2-2. Knight KG-2100 D-C Oscilloscope

The Knight KG-2100 Oscilloscope (Allied Radio) is designed for both laboratory and service work. (See Fig. 2-2.) The single-channel dc to 5 MHz vertical system provides calibrated deflection factors from 50 millivolts (5 millivolts on ac) to 20 volts/division. Horizontal sweep range is adjustable from 200 nanosec/centimeter down to 0.1 sec/cm. Triggering sensitivity is 200 millivolts external and 0.5 cm internal.

The following paragraphs describe the function or operation of the controls and connectors, together with comments on how these controls relate to controls on the Tektronix Type 453 Oscilloscope described earlier.

The functions of the astigmatism, focus, intensity, illumination, vertical position, and horizontal position controls are indentical with those of the Type 453.

The volts/cm selector and variable control are similar to the Type 453 volts/div and variable controls, except for the calibration scales.

The a-c–d-c switch is similar to the Type 453 a-c GND d-c switch, except that there is no ground (GND) position. Therefore, the input signal cannot be grounded except by external means.

The vertical in connector is identical to the Type 453 input connector; it provides for input of the vertical signal.

The trigger input switch is similar in function to the Type 453 source switch, with certain exceptions. In the int a-c position, the d-c component of the trigger signal is blocked, and the sweep is triggered by the vertical input. In the int d-c position, the sweep is also triggered by the vertical input, but by low-frequency signals which would be attenuated in the int a-c position. In the ext a-c position, the d-c component of the trigger signal is blocked, and the sweep is triggered by an external signal applied to the ext trigger connector. In the ext d-c position, the sweep is also triggered by an external source, but by low-frequency signals which would be attenuated in the ext a-c position. In the line position, a sample of the power-line frequency is connected to the trigger generator (and thus to the horizontal sweep oscillator).

The horizontal amp switch is similar in basic function to the Type 453 sweep mode switch in that it determines the sweep operating mode, but four positions are provided: int X1 and int X5 (internal linear sawtooth sweep), ext sig (external signal), and line (line-frequency sine wave).

The trigger slope and trigger level switches are identical in function to the Type 453 slope and level switches, respectively.

The time/cm selector and variable control are similar to the Type 453 time/div and variable controls, except for the calibration scales.

The 0.1 volt P-P connector is similar to the Type 453 1 KC cal connector, except that the calibration output voltage is 0.1 volt peak-to-peak sine wave instead of square wave.

The horizontal connectors provide two functions. The center or common connector and the ext sig connector provide for input of an external signal to the horizontal amplifier or sweep circuit. The common connector and the ext cap connector provide for connection of an external capacitor to the horizontal sweep oscillator. This provides for very slow sweeps, as determined by the capacity of the capacitor. There is no comparable function on the Type 453.

2-3. Miscellaneous Operating Controls

In addition to the controls of major importance described in Sections 2-1 and 2-2, other controls must be adjusted for proper oscilloscope performance. On some oscilloscopes, these additional functions are adjusted by front-panel controls; on other instruments, the function is set by a screwdriver adjustment.

One front-panel control, found particularly on oscilloscopes used for TV service, is a "phasing control." Adjustment of this control varies the horizontal sweep when it is being driven by the line voltage at the line frequency. The "phasing control" is especially important when the oscilloscope is used with a sweep generator (driven at line frequency) to observe a response pattern of a tuned circuit or amplifier. If there is a phase shift between the sweep generator and horizontal sweep, even though they are at the same frequency, a double pattern will appear, as shown in Fig. 2-5. This condition can be corrected by shifting the oscilloscope sweep drive signal phase.

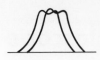

Fig. 2-5. Double RF response curve caused by improper setting of phasing control (no blanking used).

The following additional controls or adjustments are found in many oscilloscopes:

VOLTAGE REGULATION. Sets the output voltage of regulated power supplies in oscilloscopes.

CALIBRATION VOLTAGE. Sets the calibration voltage output.

SWEEP FREQUENCY. Sets the horizontal sweep oscillator frequencies to match the sweep selector switch calibrations.

D-C BALANCE. Balances the d-c amplifiers for trace centering.

LINEARITY. Sets linear horizontal and vertical deflection on each side of the screen center.

FREQUENCY COMPENSATION. Sets amplifier and attenuator components (vertical and horizontal) for wide-band response.

HUM BALANCE. Cancels power supply hum.

CHAPTER 3

Oscilloscope
Specifications
and Performance

This chapter discusses oscilloscope characteristics. Although this text is not intended as a "theory book" or an oscilloscope circuits book, it assumes a working knowledge of oscilloscope characteristics enables the operator to obtain maximum benefit from his instrument. The following discussion is also intended to explain many of the technical terms used to describe oscilloscopes.

3-1. Sweeps and Scales

In most cases, oscilloscopes have built-in sawtooth sweep generators which produce constant-speed horizontal-beam deflection. In early oscilloscopes, the generators ran continuously. Horizontal calibration was based on their repetition frequency. In laboratory oscilloscopes, sweeps are usually calibrated in terms of a direct unit of time for a given distance of spot travel across the screen. This accounts for the term *time-base*.

An oscilloscope with the widest range of sweeps is usually the most versatile. The primary usefulness of an oscilloscope, however, is as a high-speed device. Fastest sweeps are usually considered adequate if they can display *one cycle of the upper passband frequency across the full horizontal scale.*

When accurate *rise-time* measurements must be made which require the fastest sweep, a useful figure of merit for the adequacy of that sweep is

$$M = \frac{T_R}{T_D}$$

where
   M = figure of merit
   T_R = vertical system (usually amplifier) rise time
   T_D = time per division of the fastest sweep

Figures of merit greater than 1 are seldom found in oscilloscopes having rise times less than approximately 30 nanoseconds. Figures of merit greater than about 6 exceed the ideal and offer no further advantage. Accurate rise-time measurements should not be attempted when the rise time of a step-signal exceeds the vertical deflection system rise time.

Time-base accuracy is usually specified in terms of the permissible full-scale sweep timing error for any calibrated sweep. That is, an accuracy of 3 per cent would mean that the actual full-scale period of any sweep should not be more than 3 per cent greater or less than indicated.

Magnified sweeps may have poorer accuracy ratings than unmagnified sweeps, since magnification is usually achieved by reducing amplifier feedback.

Portions of sweeps may be magnified by increasing the gain of the horizontal amplifier, allowing either or both ends of the sweep to go off-screen, and positioning the display so that the desired portion is on screen. This method delays the presention of a sweep portion. Another method is generating suitably delayed sweep triggering signals so that the fast sweeps may be triggered just before the moments when the signal to be examined occurs. This second method delays actual generation of the displayed sweep; it is usually the preferred method, since it provides better long-term accuracy of the displayed time-base, eliminates jitter, and provides greater time-interval measurements.

3-2. Rise Time and High-frequency Response

Rise time is the more important specification for faster oscilloscopes; and passband (bandwidth), the more frequently used specification for slower oscilloscopes. The product of rise time and frequency response should produce a factor whose value lies between 0.33 and 0.35, when transient response is optimum.

NOTE

Transient response is the faithfulness with which a deflection system displays fast-rising step-signals. The most common transient response distortions are overshoot, ringing, and reflections from impedance discontinuities in the vertical-signal delay line. These forms of distortion will make "clean" step-signals appear to have spikes, squiggles, or bumps when they actually do not. Likewise, these forms of distortion will make "unclean" signals appear worse.

In an example of combining rise time and frequency response to determine optimum transient response, the product of 0.023 microsecond rise time (0.023 × 10⁻⁶ sec) and 15 MHz (15 × 10⁶ Hz) equals 0.345. Factors less than 0.35 probably indicate overshoot in excess of 2 per cent; factors larger than 0.4 probably indicate overshoot in excess of 5 per cent. Ideally, oscilloscopes should have a vertical system capable of rising in about one-fifth the time that the fastest step-signal rises.

Signal risetime can be calculated to a close approximation by the equation:

$$T_S = \sqrt{T_I^2 - T_A^2}$$

where $T_S =$ signal rise time
        $T_I =$ indicated rise time
        $T_A =$ vertical system (usually amplifier) rise time

The accuracy of such calculations falls off sharply for signals which rise faster than the oscilloscope amplifier.

3-3. Display Geometry

Here are some common limitations and application pitfalls which apply to almost all oscilloscopes. Some easily made performance checks are also included.

3-3-1. Trace and Scale Alignment

A horizontal trace should coincide with the horizontal scale markings on the graticule. Misalignment, as shown in Fig. 3-1, usually indicates a

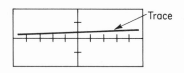

Fig. 3-1. Example of misalignment between trace and scale.

need to reorient the CRT or the scale, but may be caused by inadequate CRT shielding or the presence of a strong magnetic field. CRT's operated with low accelerating potentials are most susceptible. Even the earth's magnetic field may alter trace alignment.

3-3-2. CRT Deflection Perpendicularity

The horizontal plates should deflect the beam in a direction perpendicular to that of the vertical deflection plates. A small deviation would be less than 1 degree near the center of the screen. A 1-degree error is a displacement from perpendicular of 1 mm in 5.7 cm. Axis inaccuracy will affect the whole display geometry.

3-3-3. Trace Bowing

Beam deflection may deviate from a straight line when a trace appears near the outer limits of the useful screen area, as shown in Fig. 3-2. A CRT

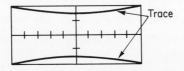

Fig. 3-2. Example (exaggerated) of trace bowing.

may be tested by using sets of horizontal or vertical lines or by manually positioning the beam rapidly back and forth, horizontally and vertically, near all four sides of the useful area. Bowing tolerance depends upon the CRT type and its operating voltages. A typical high-quality CRT will not deviate from parallel lines by more than 1 mm on the edges, nor by more than 0.5 mm at the top and bottom.

To minimize bowing, some systems have adjustable voltages on special electrodes in the CRT. Excessive bowing may be owing to improper accelerating voltage, a poor CRT, or an appreciable difference between the d-c levels of the vertical and horizontal deflection plates (with spot centered).

3-3-4. Horizontal Nonlinearity

Equal changes in voltage on the horizontal plates should produce equal changes in spot position. Any CRT nonlinearity (as shown in Fig. 3-3) that exists cannot usually be compensated for. Other nonlinearities depend upon the quality and adjustment of the sweep generator and/or horizontal amplifier.

3-3-5. Amplitude Compression

Amplitude linearity of a d-c–coupled amplifier may be checked by observing any change of amplitude of a small signal while positioning the display

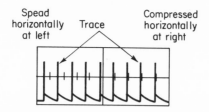

Fig. 3-3. Example (exaggerated) of horitzontal nonlinearity.

through the useful scan area. For a-c–coupled deflection plates, compression can be checked by changing the input signal by measured increments and observing whether the displayed signal amplitude changes by exactly corresponding amounts.

3-4. Position Drift

High-gain, d-c–coupled amplifiers are apt to drift appreciably. After turn-on, as much as an hour or so is sometimes required for the rate of drift to reduce to a minimum. After warmup, the maximum amount of drift to be expected is often specified in terms of millivolts (or microvolts) per hour. The amount of position change that such a drift represents depends upon the deflection factor selected. For example, if the deflection factor is 1 millivolt/cm, and the drift specification is 1 millivolt/hr, the drift in any 1-hr period should not be greater than 1 cm. In most cases, the drift per hour is of little significance, since measurements generally take no more than a minute or so.

CHAPTER 4

Oscilloscope Probes
and Accessories

Like a test meter, an oscilloscope can perform most of its functions without accessories. One exception that applies to both instruments is a probe. In fact, many of the probes used with test meters can be used with oscilloscopes. To get the full benefit from a probe, the user needs a working knowledge of how the probe performs its function, even though the actual operating procedure is quite simple. Therefore, this chapter describes the probes most commonly used with modern oscilloscopes. The chapter also describes a few other accessories that can be used effectively with both shop-type and laboratory oscilloscopes.

4-1. The Basic Oscilloscope Probe

In its simplest form, the oscilloscope probe resembles the "test prod" of a meter. It is essentially a thin metal prod connected to the oscilloscope input terminal through an insulated flexible lead. All but a small tip of the rod is covered with an insulated handle so that the probe can be connected to any point of a circuit without touching nearby circuit parts. Sometimes the probe tip is provided with an alligator clip so that it is not necessary to hold the probe at the circuit point.

Such probes work well on circuits carrying dc and audio-frequency ac.

If, however, the ac is at a high frequency, or if the gain of the oscilloscope amplifier is high, it may be necessary to use a special *low-capacitance* probe. Hand capacitance in a simple probe can cause pickup of hum, particularly if the oscilloscope amplifier gain is set high. This can be offset by shielding in a low-capacitance probe. More important, the input impedance of the oscilloscope is connected directly to the circuit under test by a simple probe and may change the circuit operation. The low-capacitance probe contains a series capacitor and resistor which increase the oscilloscope impedance.

4-2. Low-capacitance Probes

The basic circuit of a low-capacitance probe is shown in Fig. 4-1. The

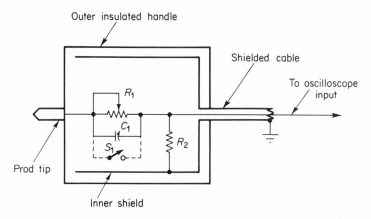

Fig 4-1. Typical low-capacitance probe circuit.

series resistance R_1 and capacitance C_1, as well as the parallel or shunt resistance R_2, are surrounded by a shielded handle. The values of R_1 and C_1 are preset at the factory by screwdriver adjustment.

In most low-capacitance probes, the values of R_1 and R_2 are selected so that they form a 10:1 voltage divider between the circuit under test and the oscilloscope input. Hence, the operator must remember that voltage indications will be one-tenth of the actual value when the probe is used.

The capacitance value of C_1, in combination with the values of R_1 and R_2, also provides a capacitance reduction from approximately 3:1 to 11:1. R_1 and C_1 are usually factory adjusted and should not be disturbed unless recalibration is required. In that event, calibration should be performed as described in the probe or oscilloscope instruction manual.

There are probes which combine the feature of low capacitance and the simple probes described in Sec. 4-1. In such probes, a switch (shows as S_1 in dotted form on Fig. 4-1) is used to short both C_1 and R_1 when a direct input is required. With S_1 open, both C_1 and R_1 are connected in series with the input, and the probe provides the low capacitance feature.

4-3. Cathode Follower Probes

The cathode follower probe also provides a means of connecting into a circuit without disturbing circuit operation. The basic circuit of a cathode follower probe is shown in Fig. 4-2. The circuit is essentially a cathode

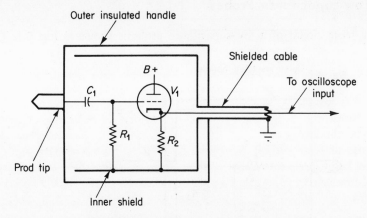

Fig. 4-2. Typical cathode follower probe circuit.

follower stage within a shielded handle. The circuit probe tip is connected to the grid input; the cathode output is connected to the oscilloscope input. The grid input resistor, R_1, is of high resistance (usually several megohms); the cathode load resistor, R_2, is of the same value as the oscilloscope input impedance. Therefore, the circuit under test sees a high impedance which does not disturb the circuit, whereas the oscilloscope sees a matched impedance. Such a circuit has one disadvantage: the cathode follower stage requires both B+ and heater power. For that reason, the cathode follower probe is used only in special applications.

4-4. Resistance-type Voltage Divider Probes

A resistance-type voltage divider probe is used when the primary concern is reduction of voltage. The resistance-type probe, shown in Fig. 4-3, is similar to the low-capacitance probe described in Sec. 4-2, except that the frequency compensating capacitor is omitted. Usually, the straight resistance-type probe is used when a voltage reduction of 100:1, or greater, is required, and when a flat frequency response is of no particular concern.

As shown in Fig. 4-3, the values of R_1 and R_2 are selected to provide

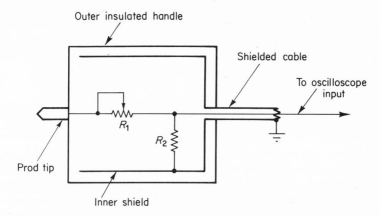

Fig. 4-3. Typical resistance-type voltage divider probe circuit.

the necessary voltage division and to match the input impedance of the oscilloscope. Resistor R_1 is usually made variable so that an exact voltage division can be obtained.

Because of their voltage reduction capabilities, resistance-type probes are often known as *high-voltage probes*. Some resistance-type probes are capable of measuring potentials at or near 40 kilovolts (with a 1000:1 voltage reduction).

4-5. Capacitance-type Voltage Divider Probes

In certain isolated cases, the resistance-type voltage divider probes described in Sec. 4-4 are not suitable for measurement of high voltages because stray conduction paths are set up by the resistors. A capacitance-type probe, shown in Fig. 4-4, can be used in those cases.

In such capacitance probes, the values of C_1 and C_2 are selected to provide

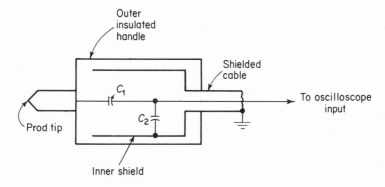

Fig. 4-4. Typical capacitance-type voltage divider probe circuit.

the necessary voltage division and to match the input capacitance of the oscilloscope. Capacitor C_1 is usually made variable so that an exact voltage division can be obtained.

4-6. Radio-frequency Probes

When the signals to be observed by an oscilloscope are at radio frequencies and are beyond the frequency capabilities of the oscilloscope amplifiers, a radio-frequency or RF probe is required. Such probes convert (rectify) the RF signals into a d-c output voltage which is equal (almost) to the peak RF voltage. The dc output of the probe is then applied to the oscilloscope input and is displayed on the screen in the normal manner. In most RF probes, the oscilloscope deflection is read as peak RF voltage. The probe circuit can be modified so that the probe dc output corresponds to the RMS value of the RF signal voltage.

The basic circuit of a radio-frequency probe is shown in Fig. 4-5. Capaci-

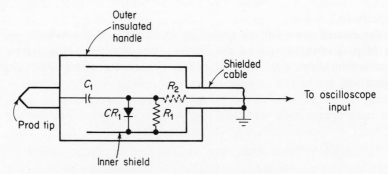

Fig. 4-5. Typical radio frequency probe circuit.

tor C_1 is a high-capacitance, d-c-blocking capacitor used to protect diode CR_1. Usually, a germanium diode is used for CR_1 which rectifies the RF voltage and produces a d-c output voltage across R_1. This d-c voltage is equal to the peak RF voltage, less whatever forward drop exists across the diode CR_1. When it is desired to produce a d-c output voltage equal to the RMS of the RF voltage, a series-dropping resistor (shown in dotted form on Fig. 4-5 as R_2) is added to the circuit. Resistor R_2 drops the d-c output voltage to a level that equals 0.707 of the peak RF value.

4-7. Demodulator Probes

The circuit of a demodulator probe (Fig. 4-6) is essentially like that of the RF probe described in Sec. 4-6. The circuit values and the basic function are somewhat different.

The prime purpose of a demodulator probe is demodulating an amplitude-modulated signal and converting the modulation envelope (low-frequency component) into a d-c output voltage.

The basic circuit of a demodulator probe is shown in Fig. 4-6. Here,

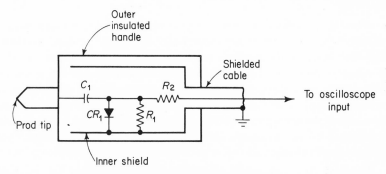

Fig. 4-6. Typical demodulator probe circuit.

capacitor C_1 is a low-capacitance, d-c blocking capacitor. (In the RF probe, a high capacitance value is required for C_1 to insure that the diode operates at the peak of the RF signal. This is not required for a demodulator probe.) Germanium diode CR_1 demodulates (or detects) the amplitude-modulated signal and produces a voltage across load resistor R_1. This voltage is pulsating dc, proportional in amplitude to the modulating voltage, and it has the same approximate waveform and frequency as the modulating voltage. Resistor R_2 is used primarily for isolation between the circuit under test and the oscilloscope input.

4-8. Using Probes Effectively

The proper use of probes is important when reliable measurements are to be made. The following notes summarize some of the more significant considerations in the use and adjustment of probes.

Probe Compensation

The capacitors which compensate for excessive attenuation of high-frequency signal components (through the probe resistance dividers) affect the entire frequency range from some midband point upwards. These capacitors must be adjusted so that the higher-frequency components will be attenuated by the same amount as low frequencies and dc. Adjustment of the compensating capacitors is a factory job and should be accomplished using the proper test equipment. It is possible, however, to check adjustment of the probe-compensating capacitors using a square-wave signal source.

First apply the square-wave signals directly to the oscilloscope input; then apply the same signals through the probe and note any change in pattern. There should be no change (except for a reduction of the amplitude) in a properly adjusted probe. Figure 4-7 shows typical square-wave displays with

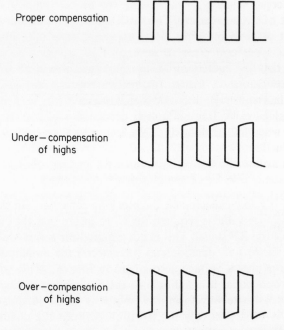

Proper compensation

Under — compensation of highs

Over — compensation of highs

Fig. 4-7. Typical square-wave displays showing frequency compensation of probes.

the probe properly compensated, undercompensated (high frequencies underemphasized) and overcompensated (high frequencies overemphasized).

Proper adjustment of probes is often neglected, especially when probes are used interchangeably with oscilloscopes having different input characteristics. It is recommended that any probe be checked with square-wave signals before use.

Another problem related to probe compensation is that input *capacitance* of the oscilloscope may change with age, or when the oscilloscope input tube is changed. Then all the compensated dividers (vertical-input step attenuator) ahead of the input tube will be improperly adjusted. Readjustment of the probe will not correct for the change needed by the other dividers of the step-attenuator. The oscilloscope circuits must be adjusted instead. Also, when compensated dividers are cascaded in step-attenuators, proper value of the resistors is especially important. Otherwise, proper compensation may not be possible at some attenuation ratios.

Circuit Loading

Connection of an oscilloscope to a circuit may alter the amplitude or waveform at the point of connection. To prevent this, the impedance of the circuit being measured must be a small fraction of the input impedance of the oscilloscope. When a probe is used, the probe's impedance determines the amount of circuit loading. The ratio of the two impedances represents the amount of probable error. For example, a ratio of 1:100 will account for about a 1 per cent error; a ratio of 1:10, about a 9 per cent error. Remember that the input impedance is not the same at all frequencies but continues to diminish at higher frequencies because of input capacitance. Even at audio frequencies, the change in impedance may be significant. When using a shielded cable, the additional capacitance of the cable should be recognized when not terminated at one end in its characteristic impedance.

The reduction of resistive loading due to probes may be as much as the attenuation ratio of the probe, but capacitive loading will not be reduced to the same extent, because of the additional capacitance of the probe cable. A typical 5:1 attenuator probe may be able to reduce capacitive loading somewhat better than 2:1. A 50:1 attenuator probe may reduce capacitive loading by about 10:1. Beyond this point, little improvement can be effected because of the stray capacitance at the probe tip.

Practical Use of Probes

Whether a particular probe connection is disturbing a circuit can be judged by attaching and detaching another connection of similar kind (such as another probe) and observing any difference in the oscilloscope display.

Long probes should be restricted to the measurement of relatively slow-changing signals. The same is true for long ground leads.

The ground lead should be connected to a point where no hum or high-frequency signal components exist in the ground path between that point and the signal pick-off point.

Reliable measurements involving frequency components higher than 10 MHz require probes with special inner conductors.

A 10-ohm resistor at the tip of a probe may prevent ringing of the ground lead when the probe is connected to very low-impedance signal sources having very high-frequency components.

Resistive loading may be eliminated entirely by using a small (0.002 microfarad or larger) capacitor in series with the probe tip, at the sacrifice of some low-frequency response.

Avoid applying more than the rated peak voltage to a probe. Using a high-voltage coupling capacitor between a probe tip and a very high d-c level may not always prevent probe burn-out, since the capacitor must charge and discharge *through the probe*. If care is taken to charge and discharge the blocking capacitor through a path which shunts the probe, the technique can be successful. A recommended procedure is permanently to attach the blocking capacitor to the probe tip and to ground the junction of the capacitor and the tip whenever the capacitor is being charged or discharged.

Check for proper probe compensation whenever changing a probe or when making an important measurement.

4-9. Electronic Switch

In many applications, it is convenient to display two signals simultaneously. (Phase measurement by the dual-trace method described in Chapter 7 is such an application.) Many laboratory-type oscilloscopes have a dual-trace provision, where two signals can be applied directly to separate oscilloscope inputs and will be displayed simultaneously. This same type of operation can be accomplished with a shop-type oscilloscope when an electronic switch, or "chopper," is used at the input. The electronic switch

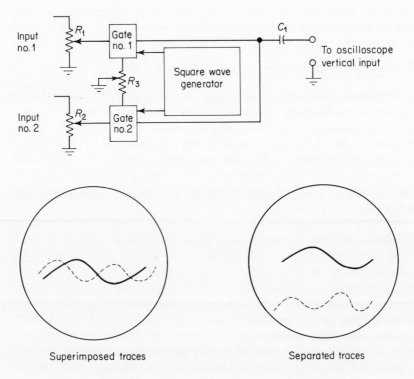

Fig. 4-8. Electronic switch circuit and typical dual-trace displays.

acts as two gates, one for each signal, which open and close on alternate half-cycles at a predetermined frequency. One gate is open while the opposite gate is closed. The output of both gates is applied to the oscilloscope input. Therefore, both signals are displayed on the oscilloscope. In practice, the gate-switching frequency must be much higher than either signal frequency.

The basic circuit of a typical electronic switch is shown in Fig. 4-8. Each signal is applied to a separate gain control and gate stage. The gate stages are alternately biased to cutoff by square-wave signals from the square-wave generator. Therefore, only one gate stage is in a condition to pass its signal at any given time. The output of both gates is applied directly to the oscilloscope input.

Figure 4-8 also shows some typical dual-trace displays. Actually, each trace is composed of a tiny bit of the corresponding signal. Since the switching rate is fast, the trace appears as a solid line. Most electronic switches are provided with some form of positioning control so that the traces can be superimposed or separated, whichever is more convenient. (The positioning control is shown as R_3 in Fig. 4-8.) Also, so that the amplitude (or height) of both signals can be made to appear approximately the same on the display despite an actual difference in signal strength, the electronic switch is provided with separate gain controls (R_1 and R_2).

4-10. Other Accessories

Many accessories besides probes and an electronic switch are available for use with oscilloscopes. Some of these are highly specialized units, such as diode or transistor switching-time testers. Other accessories are essentially extensions of the oscilloscopes, such as wide-band amplifiers and time-base units with extended ranges. Still other oscilloscope accessories are basically test instruments that can be used on their own, such as square-wave generators, pulse generators, power supplies, time-mark generators, calibrators, and spectrum analyzers.

The basic operating principles, as well as detailed operating procedures, for these specialized accessories are described in the instruction manuals for the accessories, or in the manuals for the oscilloscopes with which the accessories are to be used. Therefore, oscilloscope accessories are not covered in further detail here. When accessories are required to perform the procedures discussed elsewhere in this book, the operating procedures and test connections for the accessories are described in the relevant chapters.

Plug-in accessories are often used to extend the usefulness of laboratory-type oscilloscopes. In this case, the basic oscilloscope consists of a cathode-ray tube and power circuits. The remaining circuits (such as amplifiers, sweep generators, time-base generators, trigger circuits) are contained in plug-in units. These plug-in units can be changed to perform specific tests. In laboratory work it is usual to employ the basic oscilloscope and those accessory plug-ins required for routine or essential operation (vertical and horizontal amplifiers, horizontal sweep generator). Then, as new work areas are developed, additional plug-ins are obtained to meet their needs.

CHAPTER 5

Basic Operating Procedures and Recording Methods

The basic operating procedures of the various types of oscilloscopes described in Chapters 2 and 3 are discussed in this chapter; it also covers the basic methods for recording oscilloscope displays. Because of the great variety of oscilloscopes available, it is impossible to discuss the procedures for each make and model. Instead, typical units are described.

Later chapters describe how to use each type of oscilloscope to perform specific tests, alignments, and adjustments. There one finds instructions, such as "place oscilloscope in operation" or "set calibrating voltage to desired value." It is assumed that the operator will become familiar with his particular equipment. This is absolutely essential, since the procedures given in this chapter can be used only as a general guide to operating oscilloscope controls. The operator must understand each and every control on his particular equipment in order to follow the instructions of later chapters. No amount of textbook instruction will make the operator an expert in operating oscilloscopes; it takes actual practice. A thorough study of this chapter and a study of the controls on your particular instrument will put you on the right track.

NOTE

It is recommended that you establish a routine operating procedure, or sequence of operation, for each oscilloscope in the shop or laboratory. This will save time and will familiarize you with the capabilities and limitations of your particular equipment, thus eliminating false conclusions based on unknown operating characteristics.

5-1. Placing an Oscilloscope in Operation

The first step in placing an oscilloscope in operation is reading the instruction manual for the particular oscilloscope. Although most instruction manuals are weak in applications data, they do describe turn-on, turn-off, and the logical sequence for operating controls; hence the manual is of great help here, particularly if the operator is not familiar with the instrument.

After the manual's set-up instructions have been digested, they can be compared with the following procedures. Remember that the procedures set down in this chapter are general or typical and applicable regardless of the test which is to be performed or the type of oscilloscope used. On the other hand, instruction-manual procedures apply to the specific instrument. Therefore, if there is a conflict between the manual procedures and the following instructions, follow the manual.

NOTE

Throughout the following chapters, the direction "place oscilloscope in operation (Chapter 5)" is used frequently. This direction refers to the following procedure which has been put in this chapter to avoid repetition:

1. Set the power switch to off.
2. Set the internal recurrent sweep to off.
3. Set the focus, gain, intensity, and sync controls to their lowest position (usually full counterclockwise).
4. Set the sweep selector to external.
5. Set the vertical and horizontal position controls to their approximate midpoint.
6. Set the power switch to on. It is assumed that the power cord has been connected.
7. After a suitable warm-up period (as recommended by the instruction manual), adjust the intensity control until the trace spot appears on the screen. If a spot is not visible at any setting of the intensity control, the spot is probably off screen (unless the oscilloscope is defective). If necessary, use the vertical and horizontal position controls to bring the spot into view. *Always* use the lowest setting of the intensity control needed to see the spot. This will prevent burning the oscilloscope screen.

NOTE

The warm-up period of a d-c oscilloscope will be longer than that of an a-c oscilloscope, assuming that direct-coupled amplifiers are used in the d-c oscilloscope. Where a 1-min warm-up should be adequate for an a-c oscilloscope, most d-c oscilloscopes require 5 min. Also, many direct-coupled amplifiers will continue to drift for an hour or so after turn-on, as discussed in Chapter 3. Of course, if the oscilloscope uses all solid-state circuits, warm-up time is almost instantaneous and drift is at a minimum.

8. Set the focus control for a sharp, fine dot.
9. Set the vertical and horizontal position controls to center the spot on the screen.
10. Set the sweep selector to internal. This should be the linear internal sweep, if more than one internal sweep is available.
11. Set the internal recurrent sweep to on. Set the sweep frequency to any frequency, or recurrent rate, higher than 100 Hz.
12. Adjust the horizontal gain control and check that the spot is expanded into a horizontal trace or line. The line length should be controllable by adjusting the horizontal gain control.
13. Return the horizontal gain control to zero (or its lowest setting). Set the internal recurrent sweep to off.
14. Set the vertical gain control to the approximate midpoint. Touch the vertical input with your finger. The stray signal pickup should cause the spot to be deflected vertically into a trace or line. Check that the line length is controllable by adjustment of the vertical gain control.
15. Return the vertical gain control to zero (or its lowest setting).
16. Set the internal recurrent sweep to on. Advance the horizontal gain control to expand the spot into a horizontal line.
17. If required, connect a probe to the vertical input.
18. The oscilloscope should now be ready for immediate use. Proceed with the detailed tests as described in later chapters.

NOTE

Depending upon the test to be performed, the oscilloscope may require calibration. Voltage and current calibration procedures are described in Chapter 6.

5-2. Basic Operating Procedure

Since an oscilloscope is essentially an item of test equipment, certain precautions must be observed during its operation. Many of the precautions are the same as those to be observed for a meter or signal generator; other precautions are unique to oscilloscopes. Some of the precautions are designed to prevent damage to the oscilloscope or the circuit under test; others are to prevent injury to the operator. The following precautions are divided into two groups: general safety precautions and oscilloscope operating precautions. Both should be studied thoroughly and then compared to any specific precautions called for in the oscilloscope's instruction manual.

5-2-1. General Safety Precautions

1. The metal cases of most oscilloscopes are connected to the ground of the internal circuit. For proper operation, the ground terminal of the oscilloscope should always be connected to the ground of the equipment under test. Make certain that the chassis of the equipment under test is not connected to either side of the a-c line (as is the case with some older a-c–d-c radio sets) or to any potential above ground. If there is any doubt, connect the equipment under test to the power line through an isolation transformer.

2. Remember, there is *always* danger inherent in testing electrical equipment which operates at hazardous voltages. Therefore, the operator should thoroughly familiarize himself with the equipment under test before working on it, bearing in mind that high voltages may appear at unexpected points in defective equipment.

3. It is good practice to remove power before connecting test leads to high-voltage points. In fact, it is preferable to make all test connections with the power removed. If this is impractical, be especially careful to avoid accidental contact with equipment and other objects which can provide a ground. Working with one hand in your pocket and standing on a properly insulated floor lessens the danger of shock.

4. Filter capacitors may store a charge large enough to be hazardous. Therefore, discharge filter capacitors before attaching the test leads.

5. Remember that leads with broken insulation offer the additional hazard of high voltages appearing at exposed points along the leads. Check test leads for frayed or broken insulation before working with them.

6. To lessen the danger of accidental shock, disconnect test leads immediately after the test is completed.

7. Remember that the risk of severe shock is only one of the possible hazards. Even a minor shock can place the operator in danger of more serious risks, such as a bad fall or contact with a source of higher voltage.

8. The experienced operator continuously guards against injury and does not work on hazardous circuits unless another person is available to assist in case of accident.

5-2-2. Oscilloscope Operating Precautions

1. Even if you have had considerable experience with oscilloscopes, always study the instruction manual of *any* oscilloscope with which you are not familiar.

2. Use the procedures sf Sec. 5-1 to place the oscilloscope in operation. It is good practice to go through the procedures each time that the oscilloscope is used. This is especially true when the oscilloscope is used by other persons. The operator cannot be certain that position, focus, and (especially) intensity controls are at safe positions, and the oscilloscope could be damaged by switching it on immediately.

3. As in the case of any cathode-ray tube device (such as a TV receiver), the CRT spot should be kept moving on the screen. If the spot must remain in one position, keep the intensity control as low as possible.

4. Always use the *minimum intensity* necessary for good viewing.

5. If at all possible, avoid using an oscilloscope in direct sunlight, or in a brightly lighted room. This will permit a low-intensity setting. When the oscilloscope must be used in a bright light, use the viewing hood.

6. Make all measurements in the center area of the screen. Even if the CRT is flat, there is a chance of reading errors caused by distortion at the edges.

7. Use only shielded probes. Never allow your fingers to slip down to the metal probe tip when the probe is in contact with a "hot" circuit.

8. Avoid operating an oscilloscope in strong magnetic fields. Such fields can cause distortion of the display. Most quality oscilloscopes are well shielded against magnetic interference; however, the face of the CRT is still exposed and is subject to magnetic interference.

9. Most oscilloscopes have some maximum input voltage specified in the instruction manual. Do not exceed this maximum. Also, do not exceed the maximum line voltage, or use a different power frequency.

10. Avoid operating the oscilloscope with the shield or case removed. Besides the danger of exposing high-voltage circuits (several thousand volts are used on the CRT), there is the hazard of the CRT imploding and scattering glass at high velocity.

11. Avoid vibration and mechanical shock. As is most electronic equipment, an oscilloscope is a delicate instrument.

12. If an internal fan or blower is used, make sure that it is operating. Keep ventilation air filters clean.

13. Do not attempt repair of an oscilloscope unless you are a qualified instrument technician. If you must adjust any internal controls, follow the instruction manual.

14. Study the circuit under test before making any test connections. Try to match the capabilities of the oscilloscope to the circuit under test. For example, if the circuit under test has a range of measurements to be made (a-c, d-c, RF, pulse), you must use a wide-band, d-c oscilloscope with a low-capacitance probe and possibly a demodulator probe. Do not try to measure 3 MHz signals with a 100 kHz bandwidth oscilloscope. On the other hand, it is wasteful to use a dual-trace 50 MHz laboratory oscilloscope to check out the audio sections of transistor radios.

NOTE

The most important oscilloscope operating precautions are summarized in Fig. 5-1.

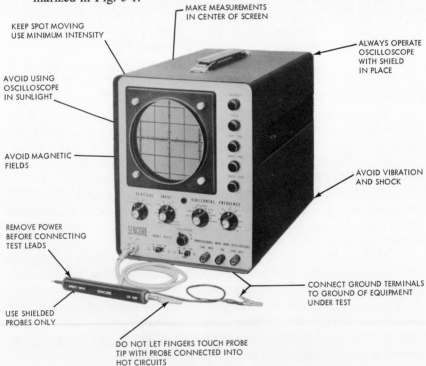

MAKE MEASUREMENTS IN CENTER OF SCREEN

KEEP SPOT MOVING USE MINIMUM INTENSITY

ALWAYS OPERATE OSCILLOSCOPE WITH SHIELD IN PLACE

AVOID USING OSCILLOSCOPE IN SUNLIGHT

AVOID MAGNETIC FIELDS

AVOID VIBRATION AND SHOCK

REMOVE POWER BEFORE CONNECTING TEST LEADS

CONNECT GROUND TERMINALS TO GROUND OF EQUIPMENT UNDER TEST

USE SHIELDED PROBES ONLY

DO NOT LET FINGERS TOUCH PROBE TIP WITH PROBE CONNECTED INTO HOT CIRCUITS

Fig. 5-1. Summary of oscilloscope operating precautions.

5-3. Recording an Oscilloscope Trace

In many applications, an oscilloscope trace must be recorded and not merely viewed. It is obviously much easier to measure and study a permanent record than an oscilloscope trace. Most recording is done with a Polaroid Land camera equipped with a special lens and a mounting frame attached to the oscilloscope. It is also possible to record with a conventional camera, with a moving film camera, or even by hand in some situations.

The following sections briefly describe the basic recording methods. (Instruction manuals for oscilloscope cameras and accessories are quite detailed about operating details and applications.)

5-4. Oscilloscope Cameras

Polaroid camera systems are most popular for oscilloscope work since they provide an immediate record with no wait for processing. One disadvantage of the early Polaroid system was that a positive print was obtained. This required special processing to obtain additional prints since no negative was available. One solution to this problem is to use a conventional camera back on the mounting frame. Graflok backs for cut film or film packs, or 120 and 620 roll film are used. Recently, negative-type Polaroid film has been available, so the use of conventional films is now limited to special applications.

Figure 5-2 is a photograph of a typical oscilloscope camera system. Figure 5-3 shows the basic operating principles of the system.

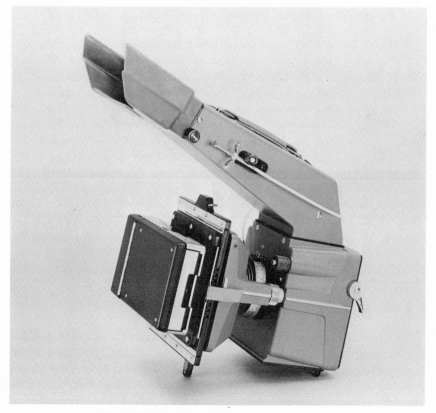

Fig. 5-2. Tektronix oscilloscope camera system.

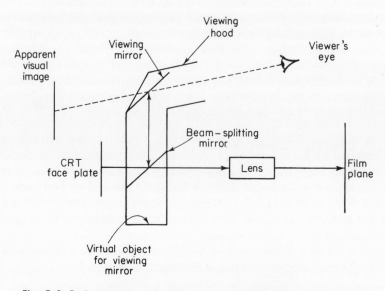

Fig. 5-3. Basic operating principles of typical oscilloscope camera system.

A special mount (bezel) is used to attach the camera to the oscilloscope. The bezel takes the place of the normal graticule cover on the oscilloscope. The optical system of the camera and attachment permits oscilloscope displays to be viewed and photographed simultaneously. Photographs are made directly from the oscilloscope screen so the image is not reversed. The viewed image is undistorted and is also not reversed. A lift-off mounting is used so that the camera can easily be mounted or removed. Swing-away hinges allow the camera to be swung out of the way when not in use. The viewing hood provides comfortable viewing with or without glasses. The rotating slide adapter allows any of the parfocal film-holding backs used with it to be locked in any of nine detented positions. All camera backs can also be rotated in 90-degree increments so that the long axis of the film will be parallel or perpendicular to the trace as desired. Several interchangeable lenses can be used with the camera when a rear casting is used. The parfocal backs allow photographs to be made on Polaroid Land or conventional film, in either sheet or roll film form.

5-4-1. Optical System Operation

As shown in Fig. 5-3, the viewing system consists of a viewing hood and two mirrors. Light from the oscilloscope screen strikes the beam-splitting mirror where a portion of the light is transmitted to the camera lens and another portion is reflected to the second mirror. A virtual image acts as the object for the second mirror surface. The second mirror then forms a virtual image which is viewed by the observer. Owing to the 45-degree arrangement of the beam-splitting mirror, the observer views the oscilloscope display as though he were looking directly toward the oscilloscope screen on a line perpendicular to the screen. This orthogonal view is full size, but the image appears approximately 20 in. away. In all cases, the lens is considerably closer to the oscilloscope screen. The difference in the two distances produces a small amount of parallax between the viewed and photographed images. The small amount of parallax can usually be ignored.

5-4-2. Selecting a Camera Back

The camera back chosen depends primarily on the intended use for the photograph; how quickly you want the finished photograph; how large an area you wish to photograph; the magnification factor of the particular lens used; and the size of the negative desired. To obtain a negative from which a number of prints can be made, either Type 55 P/N film (which comes in Polaroid Land 4 × 5 only) or conventional film is quite satisfactory. Both the Polaroid Land 4 × 5 film holder and the holders for conventional cut and roll film are used with the Graflok back in place.

With either Polaroid Land or conventional films, the size of the film used by the selected back must be at least as large as the image from the lens. This depends on the object-to-image ratio of the camera lens and on the size of the oscilloscope display. For example, the roll film back for 120 or 620 film would probably not be used with a 1 : 0.9 lens and a 10-cm-wide oscilloscope display because the image of the display is 9 cm wide and the long dimension of the film is only about 8.25 cm. Thus, at least 7.5 mm would be cut off the photograph. In practice, the film size should be at least 5 mm larger than the size of the image in order to allow for normal tolerances in the construction of the camera backs and for the position of the film in the back.

5-4-3. Writing Rate

The term *writing rate* is often used in oscilloscope photography. Writing rate is a figure of merit which roughly describes the ability of a particular camera system mounted on a particular oscilloscope to photograph fast-moving traces. The writing rate figure expresses the maximum spot rate (usually in centimeters per microsecond) which can be photographed satisfactorily. The faster the oscilloscope spot moves, the dimmer the trace becomes because the electron beam strikes each point on the phosphor coating for a shorter period of time. A camera system and oscilloscope which have a high writing rate are required for low–repetition-rate displays at the fast oscilloscope sweep rates.

It is not practical to assign an absolute value of writing rate to any oscilloscope or camera, because so many variables are involved. Among the variables which must be considered are the type of film, the CRT accelerating potential, the camera optical arrangement, the object-to-image ratio of the camera lens, and development time of the film. It is possible to compare the effectiveness of two films by measuring their writing rate under the same conditions.

Although there is some relationship between ASA rating of film and writing rate, the ASA rating is not the final determining factor. It is safe to assume that a film with a very high ASA speed rating would probably have a higher maximum writing rate than a film with a lower ASA speed rating.

5-4-4. Selecting Film

For most oscilloscope work, Polaroid Land film is convenient. This film permits the picture to be seen very soon after taking it and makes it unnecessary to expose part or all of the film before developing it.

Table 5-1 gives a brief outline of the available Polaroid emulsions. The films recommended or films having equivalent characteristics may be used.

Table 5-2 lists conventional films available, and gives a brief description of their characteristics.

5-4-5. Selecting Cathode-ray Tube Phosphors

A great number of phosphor types are presently available to the purchaser of a cathode-ray oscilloscope. No one phosphor is best for all applications; each has advantages and disadvantages compared to the others. Of the many types of phosphors available, five are most commonly in use: the P1, P2, P7, P11, and P31. Other phosphor types are usually restricted to special applications.

For low sweep rate or repetitive-sweep applications where a high writing rate is not required, almost any type of phosphor is satisfactory. Selection of the CRT phosphor is important only for single-sweep or low-repetition-rate applications at the fast sweep rates. In low-repetition-rate applications at the fast sweep rates, use of the proper phosphor can mean the difference between getting a good photograph and getting none at all.

For photographing, the most important single characteristic of a phosphor probably is the color of its emitted light. A blue or violet fluorescence has the highest actinic value and thus is most suitable for photographic work. In general (all other factors being equal), the shorter the wavelength of the visible peak emitted light, the better the phosphor for photographic applications.

Most users of oscilloscopes are concerned not only with photographing the oscilloscope trace but in observing it directly as well. For such users, it is important to have a phosphor which gives good results in both types of applications. Frequently the choice falls on a phosphor, such as P2 or P31, where the emitted light has large enough actinic value to give a good writing rate and also has sufficient persistence to permit easy viewing.

It has been observed that the P11 phosphor has the highest comparative writing rate of any common phosphor and is thus best for photographic work. The medium-short persistence of the phosphor is somewhat undesirable for general-purpose work, but the disadvantages of this are slight. Choose type P11 whenever the ultimate in photographic ability is required. Type P11 emits a blue light of medium-short duration.

Table 5-3 lists the characteristics of common phosphors.

5-4-6. Photographic Recording Techniques

The following procedures can be used to obtain an exposure for both Polaroid and conventional film, when photographing *repetitive* oscilloscope traces.

1. Position the external graticule, if any, for white lines.

NOTE

Graticule lighting should not be so high as to produce glare, but high enough to make the lines shine. This is true for almost all photographic recording, except where the exposure is very short. Medium graticule lighting for short exposures may not produce a sharp reproduction. Sometimes, this condition can be corrected by double exposure. The preferred technique is to expose the film first with the graticule only, then with the graticule and trace combined. As with most oscilloscope photography, the exposure times must be found by experiment. A dim, thin trace requires longer exposure but gives better reproduction. A bright trace can produce a "halo" or afterglow.

2. Mount the camera bezel on the oscilloscope.
3. Obtain the signal and adjust the controls for the desired display.
4. Attach the camera to the bezel and secure the camera against the oscilloscope.
5. Adjust the focus, astigmatism, and intensity controls for a sharp trace.
6. Set the aperture selector for the largest lens opening (smallest f-stop number) and carefully focus the camera on the trace or halfway between the trace and graticule.

NOTE

When using an external graticule and both clear trace and external graticule are desired, the camera should be focused halfway between the trace and graticule.

7. Set the intensity to midrange, graticule scale about three-quarters

of full range, shutter speed to 1/5 sec, and aperture selector to f/5.6. These control settings should be reasonably close for film speeds of 400 ASA and a waveform frequency near 1 kHz. For film with a 3000 ASA rating and waveform frequency of 1 kHz, use a shutter speed of 1/5 sec and an aperture selector setting of f/4.5.

The following procedures can be used to obtain an exposure when photographing *single-sweep displays.*

NOTE

Single-sweep displays are formed when the oscilloscope spot sweeps across the screen only once. Actual exposure time is thus determined not by the shutter setting but by the duration of the sweep plus phosphor persistence, provided that the shutter is open sufficiently long. In one type of single-sweep photography, the graticule exposes the film for the time set by the shutter whereas the spot on the screen exposes the film for only the duration of the sweep. Therefore, it is not usually possible to adjust the trace and graticule for the same intensity and obtain good pictures, since the effective exposure times for the two are different. Success in obtaining good photographs of single-sweep displays will come only with experience. A few tips, however, may reduce the amount of experimenting required.

8. Select a shutter speed longer than the event to be photographed. Alternatively, use the "time" or "bulb" camera position and hold the shutter open while manually triggering the sweep.
9. Use the highest possible intensity without causing defocus of the trace.
10. Where practical, use f-stops higher than f/4, if an external graticule is used. This will allow both trace and external graticule to be in focus.

NOTE

Remember that since the shutter speed has already been determined, the selection of lens opening will determine how well the trace photographs. In single-sweep applications, the camera settings must be made for trace intensity and duration. Graticule intensity cannot be used as a reference.

5-4-7. Conventional Cameras for Oscilloscope Recording

Conventional cameras can be used, with certain limitations, in place of Polaroid cameras for oscilloscope recording. The adapters used with Polaroid cameras can also be used with conventional film cameras, including 35 mm. The film must be processed in the normal manner.

It is also possible to use a conventional camera without an adapter, if several precautions are taken and if the inconvenience can be tolerated. Two basic problems are to be considered: focal length of the camera and ambient light.

Most cameras have a minimum focal length of 2 or 3 ft. This will produce a very small image on the negative, requiring blow-up of the print (with the usual distortion problems). This problem can be minimized using a camera fitted with a close-up lens. The ambient light problem can be overcome by using a cardboard tube between the oscilloscope screen and camera to exclude the light. The author has successfully used a twin-lens reflex with high-speed film (400 ASA minimum), focusing from a distance of about 12 in. through a hood or light shield. Any such arrangement is makeshift, however, and should be used as a temporary or emergency method.

5-4-8. Moving Film Cameras for Oscilloscope Recording

Moving film cameras are sometimes used in highly specialized oscilloscope work, such as studying lightning, noise, electrical breakdown, cosmic rays, metal fatigue, or any random occurrence. Moving film cameras are similar to motion picture cameras in that both have film which is drawn across the lens. In a moving film camera, the film is drawn continuously by an adjustable-speed motor, and there is no opening and closing of a shutter for each frame, as in a motion picture camera.

The moving film itself provides the horizontal sweep and the time base. Usually, the signal to be measured is applied to the oscilloscope vertical input in the normal manner, but the horizontal sweep is switched off. (Since operating a moving film camera for oscilloscope recording is so specialized, the instruction manuals provide a great amount of detail, which will not be repeated here.)

5-5. Hand Recording Oscilloscope Traces

When a camera is not available, it is possible to "hand record" oscilloscope traces. Of course, such recording is limited to traces of long duration, which will remain stationary. Also, hand recording requires considerable skill and should be used only as a temporary or emergency technique.

The oscilloscope trace can be recorded on a transparent plastic overlay cut to the same size as the oscilloscope screen. Thin paper can also be used, but this requires that the intensity be advanced.

If the plastic overlay is used, the actual trace is made with a well-sharpened grease pencil, permitting the trace to be rubbed off and the overlay reused when the particular trace is no longer needed. Attach the overlay to the screen with two-sided adhesive tape, or hold firmly in place. It is often convenient to inscribe a graticule on the overlay, and to align this graticule with that of the oscilloscope screen. The plastic overlay should be thick enough so that it does not wrinkle, but not so thick that it produces parallax (0.01 in. is usually satisfactory).

If paper is used, the actual trace is made with a medium pencil, being careful not to scratch the screen. Be careful, too, not to advance the intensity to a point where the screen could be burned. It is often convenient to use draftsman's graph paper, with a graticule ruled on one side. If possible, use a graph paper where the divisions correspond to the oscilloscope screen divisions.

NOTE

The static electricity present on plastic or paper sheets may prove a problem when placed against the oscilloscope screen. The static electricity charge can distort the display. Discharge the paper or plastic before attaching it to the oscilloscope. This can be accomplished by touching the sheet to a good ground.

TABLE 5-1

Polaroid Land Film Types

Film Type	ASA Rating (Approximate)	Picture Size	Remarks
47	300	$3\frac{1}{4} \times 4\frac{1}{4}$	Panchromatic. Paper print. Roll film only. High-speed with medium contrast.
107	3000	$3\frac{1}{4} \times 4\frac{1}{4}$	Panchromatic. Film packs only. Paper print. Similar to Type 47.
410	10,000	$3\frac{1}{4} \times 4\frac{1}{4}$	Roll only. Panchromatic type. Paper print. Extra high-speed film good for extremely fast waveforms.
46L	800	$3\frac{1}{4} \times 4\frac{1}{4}$	Roll only. Yields positive transparency. Medium contrast. High speed. Panchromatic type.
146L	125	$3\frac{1}{4} \times 4\frac{1}{4}$	Slower speed than type 46L; faster development time. Roll only. Positive transparency. High contrast.
52	200	4×5	Sheet only. Panchromatic type. Yields paper print. Good general-purpose film.
55 P/N	50	4×5	Positive paper print and reproducible negative. Sheet form. Panchromatic type. High-resolution negative.
57	300	4×5	Panchromatic type. Sheet only. Paper print. Equivalent of Type 47 in sheet form.
48	75	$3\frac{1}{4} \times 4\frac{1}{4}$	Color film which yields a paper print. Available in roll only. Requires no coating.
58	75	4×5	Color film which yields a paper print. Available in sheet only. Requires no coating.
108	75	$3\frac{1}{4} \times 4\frac{1}{4}$	Color film which yields a paper print. Available in film packs only. Requires no coating.

Types 47, 107, 410, 146L, 52, 57 require 10 sec development time. Type 46L requires 2 min development time. Type 55P/N requires 20 sec development time. Types 48, 58, and 108 require 50–60 sec development time.

TABLE 5-2

Conventional Film Types

Manufacturer	Film Name	ASA Rating	Remarks
Eastman Kodak	Tri-x	400	High speed, medium contrast. Roll film.
	RS Pan	650	Similar to Tri-x, in sheet form.
	Royal-x Pan	1250	Ultra-fast roll film with low contrast.
	Recording Royal-x Pan	1250	Same as Royal-x Pan Recording in sheet form.
	Plus-x Pan	160	Medium-speed film with good contrast. Both sheet and roll film.
Agfa	Isopan Record	1000	High-speed film with low contrast. Both sheet and roll film.
Ansco	Super Hypan	400	Medium-speed film with medium contrast. Both sheet and film.

TABLE 5-3

Common Phosphor Table

Phosphor Type	Writing Rate (Per-cent of P11, used as standard)	Relative Brightness (per cent)	Color	
			Fluorescence	Phosphorescence
P1	35	150	Yellowish-green	Yellowish-green
P2	70	230	Bluish-green	Green
P7	95	128	Blue-white	Yellowish-green
P11	100	100	Purplish-blue	Purplish-blue
P31	75	390	Green	Green

CHAPTER 6

Measuring Voltage
and Current

The oscilloscope has both advantages and disadvantages when used to measure voltage and current. The most obvious advantage is that the oscilloscope shows waveform, frequency, and phase simultaneously with the amplitude of the voltage or current being measured. The volt-ohmmeter or electronic voltmeter shows only amplitude. Likewise, most meters are calibrated in relation to sine waves. When the signals being measured contain significant harmonics, the calibrations are inaccurate. With the oscilloscope, the voltage is measured from the displayed wave which includes any harmonic content. In certain applications, the lack of inertia and high-speed response of an oscilloscope make it the only instrument capable of transient voltage measurement.

The only major disadvantage of using an oscilloscope for voltage and current measurement is the problem of resolution. The scales of simple, inexpensive volt-ohmmeters or electronic voltmeters are easier to read than the graticules of an oscilloscope. In most cases, the vertical oscilloscope scales are used for voltage and current measurements, with each scale division representing a given value of voltage or current. Where voltages are large, it is difficult to interpolate between divisions.

Another problem, although not a disadvantage, is that voltages measured with an oscilloscope are peak-to-peak, whereas most voltages specified in electronic maintenance and troubleshooting manuals are RMS. This requires that the peak-to-peak value be converted to RMS.

To sum up, if the only value of interest is voltage or current amplitude, use the meter because of its simplicity in read-out. Use the oscilloscope where waveshape characteristics are of equal importance to amplitude.

This chapter describes the procedures for measuring both a-c and d-c voltages and currents with an oscilloscope. The screen of any oscilloscope must be calibrated before accurate voltage and current measurments can be made. Laboratory oscilloscopes are calibrated against precision standards. The instruction manuals for laboratory oscilloscopes describe the calibration procedures in great detail. Shop oscilloscopes are often calibrated against any available standard. Often, shop oscilloscope manuals are somewhat sketchy on calibration details. Consequently, this chapter includes calibration procedures directed to shop oscilloscope users, but which can also apply to the laboratory oscilloscope.

NOTE

The vertical amplifier of a laboratory oscilloscope usually has a step-attenuator where each step is related to a specific deflection factor (such as volts/cm). These oscilloscopes need not be calibrated for voltage or current measurements since calibration is an internal adjustment performed as part of routine maintenance. The vertical amplifiers of shop oscilloscopes usually have variable attenuators, and possibly a step-attenuator. The steps do not, however, have a specific volts/cm deflection factor. Such oscilloscopes must be calibrated before they can be used to measure voltage and current. Therefore, the procedures for both types of oscilloscopes are given in this chapter, where the procedures differ.

6-1. Peak-to-Peak Measurements
A-C Laboratory Oscilloscope

1. Connect the equipment as shown in Fig. 6-1.
2. Place the oscilloscope in operation (Chapter 5).
3. Set the vertical step-attenuator to a deflection factor which will allow the expected signal to be displayed without overdriving the vertical amplifier.
4. Set the input selector to measure ac. Connect the probe to the signal being measured.
5. Switch on the oscilloscope internal recurrent sweep.
6. Adjust the sweep frequency for several cycles on the screen.
7. Adjust the horizontal gain control to spread the pattern over as much of the screen as desired.
8. Adjust the vertical position control so the downward excursion of

the waveform coincides with one of the graticule lines below the graticule center line, as shown in Fig. 6-1.

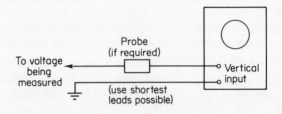

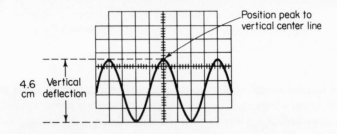

Fig. 6-1. Measuring peak-to-peak voltages.

9. Adjust the horizontal position control so that one of the upper peaks of the signal lies near the vertical center line, as shown in Fig. 6-1.

10. Measure the peak-to-peak vertical deflection in centimeters.

NOTE

This technique may also be used to make vertical measurements between two corresponding points on the waveform, other than peak-to-peak. The peak-to-peak points are usually easier to measure.

11. Multiply the distance measured in Step 10 by the vertical attenuator switch setting. Also include the attenuation factor of the probe, if any.

Example: Assume a peak-to-peak vertical deflection of 4.6 cm (Fig. 6-1) using a 10X attenuator probe and a vertical deflection factor of 0.5 volt/cm. Using the equation:

$$\frac{\text{volts}}{\text{peak-to-peak}} = \frac{\text{vertical}}{\text{deflection}} \times \frac{\text{volts/cm}}{\text{factor}} \times \frac{\text{probe}}{\text{attenuation}}$$

Substituting the given values,

$$\text{volts peak-to-peak} = 4.6 \times 0.5 \times 10 = 23 \text{ volts}$$

NOTE

If the voltage being measured is a sine wave, the peak-to-peak value can be converted to peak, RMS, or average, as shown in Fig. 6-2. Similarly, if a peak, RMS, or average value is given and must be measured on an oscilloscope, Fig. 6-2 can be used to find the corresponding peak-to-peak value.

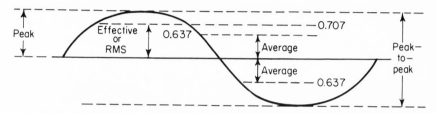

	To Get			
Given	Average	Effective (RMS)	Peak	Peak–to–peak
Average	—	1.11	1.57	1.271
Effective (RMS)	0.900	—	1.411	2.8231
Peak	0.637	0.707	—	2.00
Peak-to-peak	0.3181	0.3541	0.500	—

Fig. 6-2. Relationship of average, effective RMS, peak and peak-to-peak values for alernating current sine waves.

6-2. Peak-to-peak Measurements
A-C Shop Oscilloscope

1. Connect the equipment as shown in Fig. 6-1.
2. Place the oscilloscope in operation (Chapter 5).
3. Set the vertical gain control to the calibrate-set position, as determined during the calibration procedure (refer to Sec. 6-5).
4. Set the input selector (if any) to measure ac. Connect the probe to the signal being measured.
5. Switch on the oscilloscope internal recurrent sweep.
6. Adjust the sweep frequency for several cycles on the screen.
7. Adjust the horizontal control to spread the pattern over as much of the screen as desired.

8. Adjust the vertical position control so the downward excursion of the waveform coincides with one of the graticule lines below the graticule center line, as shown in Fig. 6-1.

NOTE

Do not move the vertical gain control from the calibrate-set position. Use the vertical position control only.

9. Adjust the horizontal position control so that one of the upper peaks of the signal lies near the vertical center line, as shown in Fig. 6-1.
10. Measure the peak-to-peak vertical deflection in centimeters.

NOTE

This technique may also be used to make vertical measurements between two corresponding points on the waveform, other than peak-to-peak. The peak-to-peak points are usually easier to measure.

11. Multiply the distance measured in Step 10 by the calibration factor (volts/cm) established during calibration. Also include the attenuation factor of the probe (if any) and the setting of the attenuator step switch (if any).

Example: Assume a peak-to-peak vertical deflection of 4.6 cm (Fig. 6-1) using a 10X attenuator probe, a 10X position of the step attenuator, and a calibration factor of 0.5 volt per centimeter.

Using the equation:

$$\frac{\text{volts}}{\text{peak-to-peak}} = \frac{\text{vertical}}{\text{deflection}} \times \frac{\text{calibration}}{(\text{volts/cm})} \times \frac{\text{probe}}{\text{attenuation}} \times \frac{\text{step switch}}{\text{attenuation}}$$
$$\text{factor} \qquad \text{factor} \qquad \text{factor} \qquad \text{factor}$$

Substituting the given values,

$$\text{volts peak-to-peak} = 4.6 \times 0.5 \times 10 \times 10 = 230 \text{ volts}$$

NOTE

If the voltage being measured is a sine wave, the peak-to-peak value can be converted to peak, RMS, or average, as shown in Fig. 6-2. If a peak, RMS, or average value is given and must be measured on an oscilloscope, Fig. 6-2 can be used to find the corresponding peak-to-peak value.

6-3. Instantaneous Voltage Measurements—D-C Laboratory Oscilloscope

1. Connect the equipment as shown in Fig. 6-3.
2. Place the oscilloscope in operation (Chapter 5).
3. Set the vertical step-attenuator to a deflection factor which will

allow the expected signal, plus any dc, to be displayed without over-driving the vertical amplifier.

4. Set the input selector to ground.

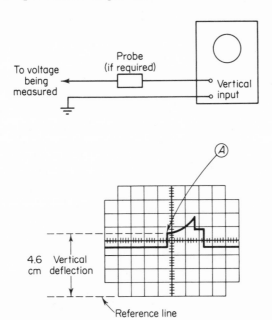

Fig. 6-3. Measuring instantaneous (or D-C) voltages.

NOTE

On most laboratory oscilloscopes, the input switch that selects either a-c or d-c measurement also has a position which connects both vertical input terminals to ground (or shorts them together). If no such switch position is provided, short the vertical input terminals by connecting the probe (or other lead) to ground.

5. Switch on the oscilloscope internal recurrent sweep. Adjust the horizontal gain control to spread the trace over as much of the screen as desired.

6. Using the vertical position control, position the trace to a line of the graticule below the center line, as shown in Fig. 6-3. This establishes the reference line. If the average signal (a-c plus d-c) is negative with respect to ground, position the trace to a reference line above the graticule center line. *Do not* move the vertical position control after this reference line has been established.

NOTE

To measure a voltage level with respect to a voltage other than ground, make the following changes in Steps 4 and 6: set the input selector to measure dc; apply the reference voltage to the vertical input; then position the trace to the reference line.

7. Set the input selector switch to dc. The ground reference line, if used, can be checked at any time by switching the input selector to the ground position. Connect the probe to the signal being measured.

8. If the waveform is outside the viewing area, set the vertical step-attenuator so that the waveform is visible.

9. Adjust the sweep frequency and horizontal gain controls to display the desired waveform.

10. Measure the distance in centimeters between the reference line and the point on the waveform at which the d-c level is to be measured. For example, in Fig. 6-3, the measurement is made between the reference line and point *A*.

11. Establish polarity of the signal. Any signal-inverting switches on the oscilloscope must be in the normal position. If the waveform is above the reference line, the voltage is positive; below the line, negative.

12. Multiply the distance measured in Step 10 by the vertical attenuator switch setting. Also include the attenuation factor of the probe, if any.

Example: Assume that the vertical distance measured is 4.6 cm (Fig. 6-3). The waveform is above the reference line, using a 10X attenuator probe and a vertical deflection factor of 2 volts/cm.

Using the equation:

$$\begin{matrix} \text{instantaneous} \\ \text{voltage} \end{matrix} = \begin{matrix} \text{vertical} \\ \text{distance} \\ \text{(in cm)} \end{matrix} \times \text{polarity} \times \begin{matrix} \text{volts/cm} \\ \text{factor} \end{matrix} \times \begin{matrix} \text{probe attenuation} \\ \text{factor} \end{matrix}$$

Substituting the given values,

$$\text{instantaneous voltage} = 4.6 \times + 1 \times 2 \times 10$$

The instantaneous voltage is +92 volts.

6-4. Instantaneous Voltage Measurements—D-C Shop Oscilloscope

1. Connect the equipment as shown in Fig. 6-3.

2. Place the oscilloscope in operation (Chapter 5).

3. Set the vertical gain control to the calibrate-set position, as determined during the calibration procedure. (Refer to Sec. 6-5.)

4. Set the input selector (if any) to ground. If no such switch position is provided, short the vertical input terminals by connecting the probe (or other lead) to ground.

5. Switch on the oscilloscope internal recurrent sweep. Adjust the

horizontal gain control to spread the trace over as much of the screen as desired.

6. Using the vertical position control, position the trace to a line of the graticule below the graticule center line, as shown in Fig. 6-3. This establishes the reference line. If the average signal (a-c plus d-c) is negative with respect to ground, position the trace to a reference line above the graticule center line. *Do not* move the vertical position control after this reference line has been established.

NOTE

To measure a voltage level with respect to a voltage other than ground, make the following changes in Steps 4 and 6: instead of shorting the vertical input terminals, apply the reference voltage to the vertical input; then position the trace to the reference line.

7. Set the input selector (if any) to dc. (The oscilloscope must be capable of d-c measurement. Some shop-type oscilloscopes do not have this capability.) The ground reference line, if used, can be checked at any time by switching the input selector to the ground position. Connect the probe to the signal being measured.

8. If the waveform is outside the viewing area, set the vertical step-attenuator (if any) so the waveform is visible. Do not move the vertical position or vertical gain controls to bring the waveform into view.

9. Adjust the sweep frequency and horizontal gain controls to display the desired waveforms.

10. Measure the distance in centimeters between the reference line and the point on the waveform at which the d-c level is to be measured. For example, in Fig. 6-3, the measurement is made between the reference line and point *A*.

11. Establish polarity of the signal. Any signal-inverting switches on the oscilloscope must be in the normal position. If the waveform is above the reference line, the voltage is positive; below the line, negative.

12. Multiply the distance measured in Step 10 by the calibration factor (volts/cm) established during calibration. Also include the attenuation factor of the probe, if any, and the setting of the attenuator step switch, if any.

Example: Assume that the vertical distance measured is 4.6 cm (Fig. 6-3). The waveform is above the reference line, using a 20X attenuator probe, a 10X position of the step-attenuator, and a calibration factor of 2 volts/cm. Using the equation:

instantaneous voltage

$$= \begin{matrix} \text{vertical} \\ \text{distance} \\ \text{(in cm)} \end{matrix} \times \text{polarity} \times \begin{matrix} \text{calibration} \\ \text{volts/cm} \\ \text{factor} \end{matrix} \times \begin{matrix} \text{probe} \\ \text{attenuation} \\ \text{factor} \end{matrix} \times \begin{matrix} \text{step switch} \\ \text{attenuation} \\ \text{factor} \end{matrix}$$

Substituting the given values,

$$\text{instantaneous voltage} = 4.6 \times +1 \times 2 \times 10 \times 10$$

The instantaneous voltage is +920 volts.

6-5. Calibrating the Vertical Amplifier for Voltage Measurements

On those laboratory oscilloscopes which have a vertical step-attenuator related to some specific deflection factor (volt/cm), the calibration procedure is an internal adjustment accomplished as part of routine maintenance. On other oscilloscopes, the vertical amplifier must be calibrated for voltage measurements. The basic calibration procedure consists of applying a reference voltage of known amplitude to the vertical input and adjusting the vertical gain control for specific deflection. Then the reference voltage is removed and the test voltages are measured, *without* changing the vertical gain setting. The calibration will remain accurate so long as the vertical gain control is at this "calibrate-set" position.

The vertical amplifier can be voltage-calibrated by several methods. For example, the calibrating voltage can be a-c or d-c, variable or fixed, internal or external. The method used depends upon the type of oscilloscope and the available calibrating voltage. The following sections describe each of the methods in turn.

6-5-1. Voltage Calibration with External DC

On oscilloscopes that do not have internal voltage reference sources, it is necessary to use an external calibrator. Any d-c source of known accuracy can be used. It is best to select an approximate calibrating voltage value that will produce at least half-scale deflection with the vertical gain control near midscale and the step attenuator (if any) is the X1 position. (This permits the step-attenuator multiplier function to be used.)

NOTE

The important point to remember concerning the external calibrating voltage is its accuracy. Accuracy of the oscilloscope voltage measurements will be no greater than the accuracy of the calibrating voltage.

1. Connect the equipment as shown in Fig. 6-4.
2. Place the oscilloscope in operation (Chapter 5).
3. Using the vertical position control, position the trace to the graticule horizontal center line.

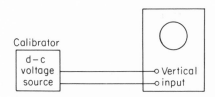

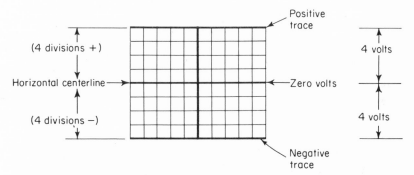

Fig. 6-4. Voltage calibration with external d-c.

NOTE

Switch the internal recurrent sweep on (for a line trace), or off (for a dot), whichever trace is most convenient for calibration.

4. Turn on the calibrator and set the calibrating voltage to the desired calibrating value.

NOTE

The exact value of the calibration voltage depends upon the graticule scale. For example, if there are eight vertical divisions (four above and four below the horizontal center line) a value of 0.4, 4, or 40 volts would be convenient.

5. Without touching the vertical position control, set the vertical gain control to move the dot or line trace vertically up to the desired number of screen divisions. For example, assuming a calibrating voltage of 4 volts and a scale as shown in Fig. 6-4, set the vertical gain control so that the trace is moved up to the top line, or four divisions from the center line. Thus, each division will equal 1 volt. In the example shown in Fig. 6-4, this would give the oscilloscope a vertical deflection factor of 1 volt/cm, with the step-attenuator set

to X1. If the step-attenuator were then moved to X10, the factor would be 10 volts/cm.

NOTE

If the external source is fixed, then the process must be reversed, and a scale factor must be selected to match the voltage. For example, assume that the only calibrating source is a 1.5-volt battery of known accuracy. The vertical gain control could then be set to provide a deflection of three divisions (from the horizontal center line up three divisions). This would give a vertical deflection factor of 0.5 volt/cm, with the step-attenuator set to X1. If the attenuator were moved to X10, the factor would be 5 volts/cm.

6. Remove the calibrating voltage and check that the trace is returned to the horizontal center line.

7. Reverse the calibrating voltage leads. Reapply the voltage and check that the trace is moved *below* the horizontal center line by the same number of divisions as obtained in Step 5.

NOTE

Thus far, the procedures have provided calibration for measurement of both positive and negative d-c voltages (positive voltages are measured above the horizontal center line; negative voltages below the center line). Where the voltages to be measured are known to be all positive (or negative), it may prove convenient to use the entire graticule scale. In that event, use the vertical position control to position the trace to the bottom graticule horizontal line (for all positive voltages), or the top horizontal line (for all negative voltages). Then apply the calibrating voltage and set the vertical gain control to move the trace vertically up (or down) the desired number of screen divisions.

8. If the calibrating source voltage is variable, check the accuracy of the calibration by applying various voltages, at various settings of the step-attenuator (if any).

NOTE

If the d-c calibrating voltage is not variable, it may be made so, using the circuit of Fig. 6-5. The accuracy of such a test configuration is entirely dependent upon the accuracy of meter M1.

9. If desired, the position of the vertical gain control should be noted and recorded as the calibrate-set position. Use this same position for all future voltage measurements. It is recommended that the calibration be checked at frequent intervals.

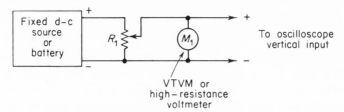

Fig. 6-5. Circuit for d-c calibration.

NOTE

Once the calibrate-set position has been established, the reference line (calibration voltage removed, zero volts) can be moved up or down as required by the vertical position control, without affecting the volts/cm factor. Remember, however, that any voltage measurements must be made from the reference line. For example, assume that the horizontal center line is used as the reference line during calibration, and the deflection factor is established as 1 volt/cm. Then, during actual voltage measurement, the reference line is moved down 2 cm below the center line, and a voltage is measured 3 cm above the center line. Since the voltage measured is 5 cm from the reference line, the correct reading would be 5 volts.

6-5-2. Voltage Calibration with External AC

On those oscilloscopes which do not have internal voltage reference sources it is necessary to use an external calibrator. Any a-c source of known accuracy can be used. It is best to select an approximate calibrating voltage value that will produce near full-scale deflection with the vertical gain control near midscale, and the step-attenuator (if any) in the X1 position. (This will permit the step-attenuator multiplier function to be used.)

NOTE

The important point to remember concerning the external calibrating voltage is its accuracy. Accuracy of the oscilloscope voltage measurements will be no greater than the accuracy of the calibrating voltage. Another point to remember is that the oscilloscope display is usually calibrated for peak-to-peak voltage, whereas the meter or other device indicating the calibrating voltage will probably be in RMS. If the calibrating voltage is a sine wave, the RMS value can be converted to peak-to-peak, as shown in Fig. 6-2. If the external calibrating voltage is a square wave or pulse, it value will be peak-to-peak.

1. Connect the equipment as shown in Fig. 6-6.
2. Place the oscilloscope in operation (Chapter 5).
3. Using the vertical position control, position the trace to the graticule horizontal center line.

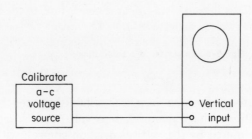

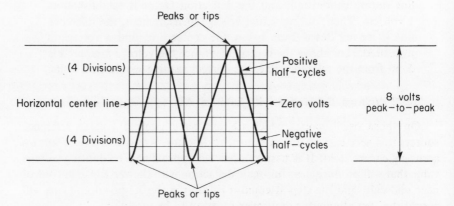

Fig. 6-6. Voltage calibration with external ac.

NOTE

Switch the internal recurrent sweep on (for a normal line trace), or off (for a dot), whichever trace is most convenient for calibration. If the internal sweep is not on, the trace will appear as a vertical line when the calibrating voltage is applied.

4. Turn on the calibrator and set the calibrating voltage to the desired calibrating value.

NOTE

The exact value of the calibrating voltage depends upon the graticule scale. For example, if there are eight vertical divisions (four above and four below the horizontal center line), a value of 0.8, 8, or 80 volts would be convenient.

5. Without touching the vertical position control, adjust the vertical gain control to align tips of positive half-cycles and tips of negative half-cycles with the desired scale divisions. For example, assuming a calibrating voltage of 8 volts peak-to-peak, and a scale as shown in Fig. 6-6, set the vertical gain control so that the trace is spread from the top line (four divisions up from the center line) to the bottom line (four divisions below the center line). Thus, each division will equal 1 volt, peak-to-peak. In the example shown in Fig. 6-6, this would give the oscilloscope a vertical deflection factor of 1 volt/cm, with the step-attenuator set to X1. If the step-attenuator were then moved to X10, the factor would be 10 volts/cm.

NOTE

If the external source is fixed, then the process must be reversed, and a scale factor must be selected to match the voltage. For example, assume that the only calibrating source is a 1-volt ac (RMS) of known accuracy. This is equal to 2.828 volts peak-to-peak. The vertical gain control could then be set to provide a spread of slightly less than three divisions (2.828 divisions). This would give a vertical deflection factor of 1 volt/cm peak-to-peak, with the step-attenuator set to X1. If the attenuator were moved to X10, the factor would be 10 volts/cm.

6. If the calibrating source voltage is variable, check the accuracy of the calibration by applying various voltages, at various settings of the step-attenuator (if any).

NOTE

If the a-c calibrating voltage is not variable, it may be made so, using the circuit of Fig. 6-7. The accuracy of such a test configuration in entirely dependent upon the accuracy of meter M1.

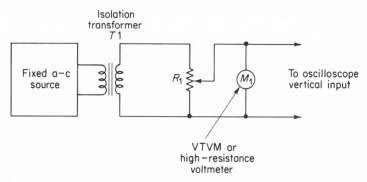

Fig. 6-7. Circuit for a-c calibration.

7. If desired, the position of the vertical gain control should be noted and recorded as the calibrate-set position. Use this same position for

all future voltage measurements. It is recommended that the calibration be checked at frequent intervals.

NOTE

Once the calibrate-set position has been established the trace can be moved up or down as required by the vertical position control, without affecting the volts/cm factor.

6-5-3. Voltage Calibration with Internal AC

Most oscilloscopes have an internal voltage source of known amplitude and accuracy available for calibration. On some oscilloscopes, this calibrating voltage is available from terminals or a jack on the front panel. On other oscilloscopes, the calibrating voltage is applied to the vertical input when one of the controls (usually the vertical input selector) is set to "calibrate" position.

1. Connect the equipment as shown in Fig. 6-8, if the calibrating voltage

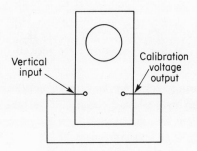

Temporary interconnection

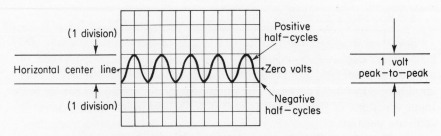

Fig. 6-8. Voltage calibration with internal ac.

is available at the front panel. If the calibrating voltage is applied by means of a control, set the control to the calibrate position.

2. Place the oscilloscope in operation (Chapter 5).

3. With the calibrate voltage removed (front-panel connections temporarily removed, or vertical input control set to normal), use the vertical position control and position the trace to the graticule horizontal center line.

NOTE

Switch the internal recurrent sweep on (for a normal line trace), or off (for a dot), whichever trace is most convenient for calibration. If the internal sweep is not on, the trace will appear as a vertical line when the calibrating voltage is applied.

4. Apply the calibrating voltage.
5. Without touching the vertical position control, adjust the vertical gain control to align tips of positive half-cycles and tips of negative half-cycles with the desired scale divisions. For example, assume a calibrating voltage of 1 volt peak-to-peak (which is typical for many oscilloscopes), set the vertical gain control so that the trace is spread from one division above the center line to one division below the center line. Thus, each division will equal 0.5 volt peak-to-peak. In the example shown in Fig. 6-8, this would give the oscilloscope a vertical deflection factor of 0.5 volt/cm, with the step-attenuator set to X1. If the step-attenuator were then moved to X10, the factor would be 5 volts/cm.
6. If desired, the position of the vertical gain control should be noted and recorded as the calibrate-set position. Use this same position for all future voltage measurements. It is recommended that the calibration be checked at frequent intervals.

NOTE

Once the calibrate-set position has been established the trace can be moved up or down as required by the vertical position control, without affecting the volts/cm factor.

6-5-4. Voltage Calibration with Internal Square Waves

Some oscilloscopes have an internal square-wave source available for calibration. Usually this source is variable in amplitude and is adjusted by a front-panel control. The square-wave amplitude is read off a scale on the amplitude adjustment control. The square waves are applied to the vertical input when one of the controls (usually the vertical input selector) is set to calibrate position.

1. Place the oscilloscope in operation (Chapter 5).
2. With the calibrate square waves removed (vertical input control set to normal), use the vertical position control and position the trace to the graticule horizontal center line.
3. Apply the calibrating square waves.

4. Set the horizontal sweep frequency to some frequency lower than that of the internal calibrating square waves.

NOTE

Several cycles of square waves should appear when the sweep frequency is lower than the internal square-wave calibrating frequency. For example, four square waves should appear if the sweep frequency is one-fourth of the calibrating frequency. One square wave should appear if the sweep frequency and calibrating frequency are the same. If the sweep frequency is considerably lower than the calibrating frequency, the flat peaks of the square waves will blend and appear as two horizontal lines. If the internal sweep is not on, the trace will appear as a vertical line when the calibrating square waves are applied.

5. Without touching the vertical position control, adjust vertical gain control and align the flat peaks of the square waves with the desired scale divisions. For example, assume square waves with a peak-to-peak amplitude of 6 volts and a scale, as shown in Fig. 6-9. Set the vertical gain control so that the square waves are spread a total of six divisions (three divisions up from the center line and three divisions below the center line). Thus, each division will equal 1 volt, peak-to-peak. In the example shown in Fig. 6-9, this would give the oscilloscope a vertical deflection factor of 1 volt/cm, with the step-attenuator set to X1. If the step-attenuator were then moved to X10, the factor would be 10 volts/cm.

NOTE

When the graticule horizontal center line is used as a reference, as described in Step 2 of this procedure, the square-wave peaks above the center line indicate positive voltage, whereas peaks below the center line indicate negative voltage. The amplitude of the square waves above (and below) the center line is equal to peak a-c voltage. This is equivalent to one-half the peak-to-peak voltage (Fig. 6-2).

6. If desired, the position of the vertical gain control should be noted and recorded as the calibrate-set position. Use this same position for all future voltage measurements. It is recommended that the calibration be checked at frequent intervals.

NOTE

Once the calibrate-set position has been established the trace can be moved up or down as required by the vertical position control without affecting the volts/cm factor.

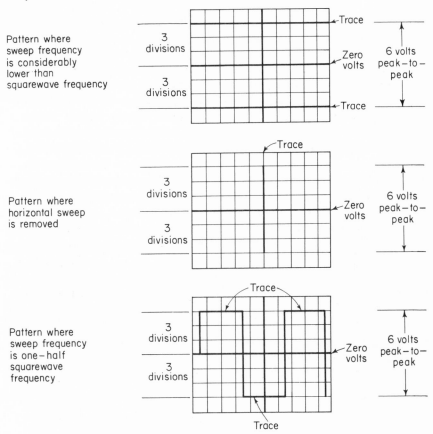

Fig. 6-9. Voltage calibration with internal square waves.

6-6. Voltage Measurements with a Variable Calibrating Source

When an oscilloscope has an internal variable calibrating voltage source, or an accurate external variable source is readily available, it is often convenient to measure voltages using the variable calibrator. This method is sometimes known as *indirect voltage measurement*. Its primary advantage is that the oscilloscope vertical amplifier and graticule screen need not be precalibrated, and the vertical gain control can be set to any convenient level. The basic procedure consists of measuring the test voltage and noting the number of divisions occupied by the trace. Then the test voltage is removed and replaced by the calibrating voltage. The calibrating voltage is adjusted until it occupies the same number of divisions as the test voltage. The calibrating voltage amplitude is read off the corresponding oscilloscope control, or the meter of the external calibrator. This method is quite accurate, but it does require continued switching back and forth between test and calibrating voltages.

The method has some other disavantages. If the calibrating voltage is internal, it may be fed directly to the vertical amplifier input when the appropriate control is set to a calibrate position, as described in Sec. 6-5-4. On such oscilloscopes, when a probe is used, it is necessary to include the probe multiplication factor. For example, assume that a voltage is measured through a 10-to-1 probe, that the test signal occupies three divisions, that the oscilloscope's internal square-wave calibrating signal is switched on and adjusted to occupy the same three divisions, and that the calibration signal-amplitude control indicates 7 volts. Since the internal calibration voltage is applied directly to the vertical input, and the test voltage is applied through a 10-to-1 probe, the actual test voltage must be 70 volts.

Another major disadvantage is that the calibrating voltage source, internal or external, may not be equal to the test voltage. This condition can be offset by means of the vertical step-attenuator, or by a voltage divider probe. For example, if the test signal may reach 300 volts, whereas the calibration source has a maximum of 30 volts, use a 10-to-1 voltage divider probe, or the X10 position of the vertical step-attenuator. Measure the test voltage with the probe (or the step-attenuator in X10); then apply the calibrating voltage with the probe removed (or the step-attenuator in X1) and adjust for the same number of divisions. Make certain to multiply the calibration voltage control indication by the appropriate factor.

NOTE

In the following procedure, it is assumed that the oscilloscope has an internal variable square-wave calibrating voltage and that the voltage to be measured is a sine wave.

1. Connect the equipment as shown in Fig. 6-10.
2. Place the oscilloscope in operation (Chapter 5).
3. Set the vertical step-attenuator and/or vertical gain control to a deflection factor which will allow the expected signal to be displayed without overdriving the vertical amplifier.
4. Set the input selector (if any) to measure ac. Connect the probe to the signal being measured.
5. Switch on the oscilloscope internal recurrent sweep.
6. Adjust the sweep frequency for several cycles on the screen.
7. Adjust the horizontal gain control to spread the pattern over as much of the screen as desired.
8. Adjust the vertical position control so the downward excursion of the waveform coincides with one of the graticule lines below the graticule center line, as shown in Fig. 6-10. Adjust the vertical gain control so that the pattern occupies an exact, easily measured number of divisions.

9. Adjust the horizontal position control so that one of the upper peaks of the signal lies near the vertical center line, as shown in Fig. 6-10.

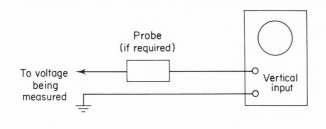

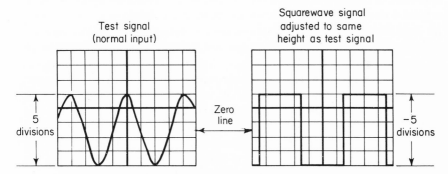

Fig. 6-10. Indirect voltage measurement with variable square-wave calibrating signal.

10. Without disturbing any of the controls, switch on the internal calibrating square-wave signals. The test signal should be removed from the screen and replaced by the square-wave calibrating signals.

11. Adjust the square-wave calibrating signal amplitude until the square-wave pattern occupies the same number of divisions as the test voltage.

NOTE

If the square-wave signal is insufficient and cannot be adjusted to occupy the same number of divisions, switch the vertical step-attenuator to a convenient multiplier scale. *Do not* move the vertical gain control.

12. Read the voltage off the calibrator amplitude control. Multiply the voltage by any probe and/or step-attenuator attenuation factor.

Example: Assume a peak-to-peak deflection factor, as shown in Fig. 6-10, using a 10X attenuator probe. Assume, too, that the calibrator amplitude control reads 3.7 volts. Further assume that the test voltage was measured with the step-attenuator in X10, and the square waves were adjusted to the same height with the step-attenuator in X1.

Using the equation:

$$\frac{\text{volts}}{\text{peak-to-peak}} = \begin{array}{c}\text{calibrator}\\\text{control}\\\text{reading}\end{array} \times \begin{array}{c}\text{probe}\\\text{attenuation}\\\text{factor}\end{array} \times \begin{array}{c}\text{difference in}\\\text{step-attenuator}\\\text{factor}\end{array}$$

Substituting the given values,

volts peak-to-peak $= 3.7 \times 10 \times 10 = 370$ volts

6-7. Composite and Pulsating Voltage Measurements

In practice, most voltages measured are composites of ac and dc, or are pulsating dc. For example, a transistor amplifier used to amplify an a-c signal will have both ac and dc on its collector. The output of a rotating d-c generator or solid-state rectifier will be pulsating, even though its polarity is constant. Such composite and pulsating voltages can be measured quite readily on an oscilloscope capable of measuring dc (as are most laboratory oscilloscopes). The procedures are essentially a combination of peak-to-peak measurements (Secs. 6-1 and 6-2) and instantaneous d-c measurements (Secs. 6-3 and 6-4). Composite and pulsating voltages can also be measured by the indirect method (Sec. 6-6). This is usually difficult. Also, since most oscilloscopes capable of measuring dc are also direct reading, the indirect method will not be discussed.

1. Connect the equipment as shown in Fig. 6-11.
2. Place the oscilloscope in operation (Chapter 5).
3. Set the vertical step-attenuator to a deflection factor which will allow the expected signal, plus any dc, to be displayed without overdriving the vertical amplifier.
4. Set the input selector to ground.

NOTE

On most laboratory oscilloscopes, the input switch that selects either a-c or d-c measurement also has a position which connects both vertical input terminals to ground (or shorts them together). If such switch position is not provided, short the vertical input terminals by connecting the probe (or other lead) to ground.

5. Switch on the oscilloscope internal recurrent sweep. Adjust the horizontal gain control to spread the trace over as much of the screen as desired.
6. Using the vertical position control, position the trace to a convenient location on the graticule screen. If the voltage to be measured is pulsating dc, the horizontal center line should be convenient. If the voltage is a composite, and the average signal (ac plus dc) is positive, position the trace below the center line. If the average is nega-

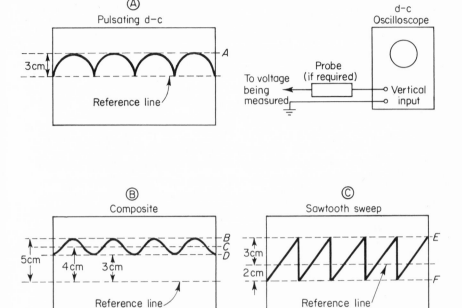

Fig. 6-11. Measurement of composite and pulsating voltages.

tive, position the trace above the center line. *Do not* move the vertical position control after this reference line has been established.

7. Set the input selector switch to dc. The ground reference line can be checked at any time by switching the input selector to the ground position. Connect the probe to the signal being measured.

8. If the waveform is outside the viewing area, set the vertical step-attenuator so the waveform is visible.

9. Adjust the sweep frequency and horizontal gain controls to display the desired waveform.

10. Establish polarity of the signal. Any signal-inverting switches on the oscilloscope must be in the normal position. If the waveform is above the reference line, the voltage is positive; below the line, negative. Measure the distance in cm between the reference line and the point on the waveform at which the level is to be measured.

NOTE

If the voltage to be measured is pulsating dc, the trace will remain on one side of the reference line, but will start and stop at the reference line, as shown in Fig. 6-11a. If the voltage is a composite of ac and dc, the trace may be on either side of the reference line; it may possibly cross over the reference line, but usually remains on one side, as shown in Fig. 6-11b. If the voltage is a non-sine wave (such as sawtooth, pulse, spike, etc.), the trace may appear on both sides of the reference line, or may be displaced above or below the line, as shown in Fig. 6-11c.

11. Multiply the distance measured in Step 10 by the vertical attenuator switch setting. Also include the attenuation factor of the probe, if any.

Example: Assume that the vertical distance measured is 3 cm from the reference line to point A of Fig. 6-11a. The waveform is above the reference line (pulsating dc), using a 10X attenuator probe and a vertical deflection factor of 2 volts/cm

Substituting the given values,

peak of the pulsating d-c voltage $= 3 \times +1 \times 2 \times 10 = 60$ volts (peak)

Example: Assume that the vertical distance measured is 3 cm from the reference line to point D (Fig. 6-11b), 4 cm to point C (Fig. 6-11b), and 5 cm to point B (Fig. 6-11b). The waveform is above the reference line (ac combined with positive dc), using a 10X attenuator probe and a vertical deflection factor of 2 volts per cm.

Substituting the given values,

d-c component (reference line to point C) $= 4 \times +1 \times 2 \times 10$
$$= +80 \text{ volts}$$

peak-to-peak of a-c component (point B to D)
$$= 2 \times 2 \times 10 = 40 \text{ volts (peak-to-peak)}$$

NOTE

The 2 cm value is obtained by subtracting the point D value (3 cm) from the point B value (5 cm).

Example: Assume that the vertical distance measured is 3 cm from the reference line to point E (Fig. 6-11c) and 2 cm from the reference line to point F. The waveform is above and below the reference line (sawtooth sweep), using a 10X attenuator probe and a vertical deflection factor of 2 volts/cm.

Substituting the given values,

positive peak of sweep (point E)
$$= 3 \times +1 \times 2 \times 10 = + 60 \text{ volts (peak)}$$

negative peak of sweep (point F)
$$= 2 \times -1 \times 2 \times 10 = -40 \text{ volts (peak)}$$

peak-to-peak of sweep (point E to F)
$$= 60 + 40 = 100 \text{ volts (peak-to-peak)}$$

6-8. Voltage Comparison
Measurements—Laboratory Oscilloscopes

In some applications, it may be necessary to establish a set of deflection factors other than those indicated by the vertical step-attenuator switch. This is useful for comparing signals to a reference voltage amplitude. To establish a new set of deflection factors based upon a specific reference amplitude, the vertical amplifier must have a variable gain control, as well as the step-attenuator.

1. Connect the equipment as shown in Fig. 6-1.
2. Place the oscilloscope in operation (Chapter 5).
3. Set the vertical step-attenuator to a deflection factor which will allow the expected signal to be displayed without overdriving the vertical amplifier.
4. Apply the reference signal of known value to the vertical input.
5. Switch on the oscilloscope internal recurrent sweep. Adjust the sweep frequency for several cycles on the screen. Adjust the horizontal gain control to spread the pattern over as much of the screen as desired.
6. Using both the vertical step-attenuator and variable gain control, adjust the display for an exact number of vertical centimeter divisions. *Do not* move the variable gain control after obtaining the desired deflection.
7. Divide the amplitude of the reference signal (volts) by the product of the deflection in centimeters (established in Step 6) and the vertical attenuator switch setting. This is the *deflection conversion factor.*

$$\begin{matrix} \text{deflection} \\ \text{conversion} \\ \text{factor} \end{matrix} = \frac{\text{reference signal amplitude (volts)}}{\text{deflection (cm)} \times \text{attenuator switch setting}}$$

8. To establish an adjusted deflection factor at any setting of the vertical attenuator switch, multiply the attenuator switch setting by the deflection conversion factor established in Step 7.

$$\begin{matrix} \text{adjusted} \\ \text{deflection} \\ \text{factor} \end{matrix} = \begin{matrix} \text{attenuator} \\ \text{switch} \\ \text{setting} \end{matrix} \times \begin{matrix} \text{deflection} \\ \text{conversion} \\ \text{factor} \end{matrix}$$

This adjusted deflection factor applies only if the variable vertical gain control is not moved from the position established in Step 6.

9. To determine the peak-to-peak amplitude of a signal compared to a reference, disconnect the reference and set the vertical step-attenuator to a deflection factor which will provide sufficient deflec-

tion to make the measurement. *Do not* move the variable gain control from the position set in Step 6.

10. Apply the signal to the vertical input and measure the deflection. The amplitude may be determined by the following:

$$\frac{\text{signal}}{\text{amplitude}} = \frac{\text{adjusted}}{\text{deflection}} \times \text{deflection (cm)}$$

Example: Assume a reference signal amplitude of 30 volts, a vertical attenuator switch setting of 5, and a deflection of 4 cm. Substituting these values in the deflection conversion factor formula (Step 7),

$$\frac{\text{deflection}}{\text{conversion}} = \frac{30}{4 \times 5} = 1.5$$
$$\text{factor}$$

Then, with a step-attenuator setting of 10, the adjusted deflection factor (Step 8) would be

$$\frac{\text{adjusted}}{\text{deflection}} = 10 \times 1.5 = 15 \text{ volts/cm}$$
$$\text{factor}$$

To determine the peak-to-peak amplitude of an applied signal which produces a vertical deflection of 5 cm, use the signal amplitude formula (Step 10):

$$\frac{\text{signal}}{\text{amplitude}} = 15 \times 5 = 75 \text{ volts}$$

6-9. Current Measurements with a Test Resistor

The most common method of measuring an unknown current is passing it through a resistance of known value, and then measuring the resultant voltage. This is the basic principle of most voltmeters. Since the oscilloscope can be used as a voltmeter, it can also be adapted to measure current. A resistor of known value and accuracy is the only other component required for the procedure. Once the voltage has been measured, the current can be calculated using the basic Ohm's law equation $I = E/R$.

1. Connect the equipment as shown in Fig. 6-12.
2. Place the oscilloscope in operation (Chapter 5).
3. Apply the current through the resistor.

NOTE

If a 1-ohm resistor is used, the calculations will be simplified. The unknown current will be equal to the measured voltage. The wattage of the resistor must be at least double the square of the maximum current (in amperes). For example, if the maximum anticipated current is 10 amp, the minimum wattage of the resistor should be $10^2 \times 2 = 200$ watts.

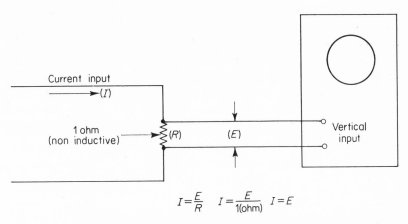

Fig. 6-12. Current measurements with a test resistor.

4. Measure the voltage drop across the resistor using the procedures of Secs. 6-1–6-4, 6-6, and 6-7, whichever is applicable to the type of voltage being measured. The unknown current will be equal to the voltage measured, provided that a 1-ohm resistance is used.

NOTE

If peak-to-peak voltage is measured, the resultant current value will also be peak-to-peak. To determine the RMS or average value, convert the measured voltage to RMS or average using Fig. 6-2

Example: Assume that the voltage drop across the 1-ohm test resistor is 10 volts peak-to-peak.

$$10 \text{ volts peak-to-peak} = 3.535 \text{ volts RMS}$$

$$I = \frac{3.535}{1} = \text{RMS current } 3.535 \text{ amp}$$

5. If the current being measured is the result of a composite voltage (ac plus dc), both the a-c and d-c voltages should be measured separately, as described in Sec. 6-7. The a-c voltage (peak-to-peak) should then be converted to RMS (using Fig. 6-2.) The d-c and a-c currents (which are equivalent to the corresponding voltages) should be combined to find the composite or total current as follows:

$$\text{total current} = \sqrt{\text{a-c current (RMS)}^2 + \text{d-c current}^2}$$

6-10. Current Measurements with a Current Probe

Measuring current with a test resistor as described in Sec. 6-9 has two disadvantages: first, the circuit must be opened so that the resistor can be inserted during the test. Second, operation of the circuit can be affected by the additional resistance. Both of these problems can be eliminated by means of a current probe. Such probes can be obtained as accessories for most laboratory oscilloscopes.

Current probes operate on the same basic principle as the clamp-type ammeters used in power electrical equipment. The basic element of a current probe is the ferrite core which is attached to a handle. Ferrite material is used to provide a wide frequency response. The core, shown functionally in Fig. 6-13, is designed to be opened and closed so that it may be clamped

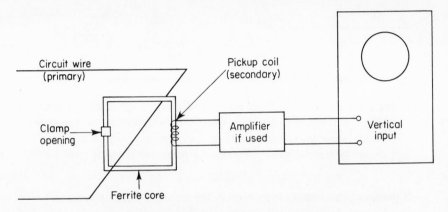

Fig. 6-13. Functional operation of current probe.

around the wire carrying the current to be measured. The wire forms the primary of a transformer. The secondary is formed by the probe pick-up coil. Current passing through the wire induces a voltage in the secondary. The secondary output voltage is usually quite high in respect to the primary, since the pick-up coil has many turns.

The probe output voltage is applied to the oscilloscope vertical input and is measured in the normal manner. Since there is a direct relationship between voltage and current, the current can be calculated from the voltage indicated on the oscilloscope. If the vertical amplifier is calibrated for a given value of reference deflection, the current may be read directly from the oscilloscope screen. For example, if the probe output is 1 millivolt per milliampere (ma) of current, and the oscilloscope vertical amplifier is calibrated from 1 millivolt per centimeter, the current may be read directly from the scale (1 ma/cm).

Very often, current probes are used with an amplifier, since the probe output is quite low in relation to the average oscilloscope deflection factor. A typical probe has an output of 1 millivolt/ma, whereas the average laboratory oscilloscope may have a vertical sensitivity of 5 millivolts/cm. Thus, it would require 50 ma to produce a deflection of 1 cm.

Since current probes are used with laboratory oscilloscopes and are provided with detailed instructions for their use, no operating procedures are given here.

CHAPTER 7

Measuring Time,
Frequency, and Phase

An oscilloscope is the ideal tool for measuring time, frequency, and phase of voltages and currents. If the horizontal sweep is calibrated directly in relation to time, such as 5 milliseconds per centimeter, the time duration of voltage waveforms may be measured directly on the screen without calculation. If the time duration of one complete cycle is measured, frequency can be calculated by simple division, since frequency is the reciprocal of the time duration of one cycle. If the oscilloscope is of the shop type where the horizontal axis is not calibrated directly in relation to time, it is still possible to obtain accurate frequency and time measurements using Lissajous figures.

Measuring phase difference between two signals is equally simple with an oscilloscope. If the instrument has two vertical inputs, the signals can be displayed simultaneously and the phase measured directly on the screen. If the oscilloscope has identical vertical and horizontal amplifiers, the phase of signals can be obtained by Lissajous figures.

This chapter describes the procedures for measuring time, frequency, and phase of a-c voltages, as well as pulse and square-wave signals.

7-1. Time-Duration Measurements—Laboratory Oscilloscopes

NOTE

The horizontal sweep circuit of a laboratory oscilloscope is usually provided with a selector control that is direct reading in relation to time. That is, each horizontal division on the oscilloscope screen has a definite relation to time, at a given position of the horizontal sweep rate switch (such as millisecond/centimeter, microsecond/centimeter). With such oscilloscopes, the waveform can be displayed, and the time duration of the complete waveform (or any portion) can be measured directly.

1. Connect the equipment as shown in Fig. 7-1.

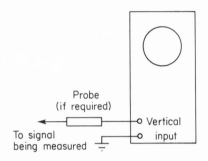

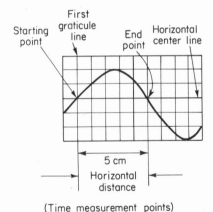

(Time measurement points)

Fig. 7-1. Measuring time duration.

2. Place the oscilloscope in operation (Chapter 5).
3. Set the vertical step-attenuator to a deflection factor which will allow the expected signal to be displayed without overdriving the vertical amplifier.
4. Connect the probe (if any) to the signal being measured.
5. Switch on the oscilloscope internal recurrent sweep. Set the horizontal sweep control to the fastest sweep rate that will display a convenient number of divisions between the time measurement points (Fig. 7-1).

NOTE

On most oscilloscopes, it is recommended that the extreme sides of the screen not be used for time-duration measurements. There may be some nonlinearity at the beginning and end of the sweep.

6. Adjust the vertical position control to move the points between which the time measurement is made to the horizontal center line.
7. Adjust the horizontal position control to move the starting point of the time measurement area to the first graticule line.
8. Measure the horizontal distance between the time measurement points (Fig. 7-1).

NOTE

If the horizontal sweep is provided with a variable control, make certain it is off or in the calibrate position.

9. Multiply the distance measured in Step 8 by the setting of the horizontal sweep control. If sweep magnification is used, divide the answer by the multiplication factor.

Example: Assume that the distance between the time measurement points is 5 cm (Fig. 7-1), the horizontal sweep control is set to 0.1 millisecond/cm, and there is no sweep magnification.

Using the equation,

$$\text{time duration} = \frac{\text{horizontal distance (cm)} \times \text{horizontal sweep setting}}{\text{magnification}}$$

Substituting the given values,

$$\text{time duration} = \frac{5 \times 0.1}{1} = 0.5 \text{ millisecond}$$

7-2. Frequency Measurements—Laboratory Oscilloscopes

NOTE

The frequency measurement of a periodically recurrent waveform is essentially the same as a time-duration measurement, except that an additional calculation must be performed. In effect, a time-duration measurement is made, then the time duration is divided into 1, or unity, since frequency of a signal is the reciprocal of one cycle.

1. Connect the equipment as shown in Fig. 7-2.
2. Place the oscilloscope in operation (Chapter 5).
3. Set the vertical step-attenuator to a deflection factor which will allow the expected signal to be displayed without overdriving the vertical amplifier.

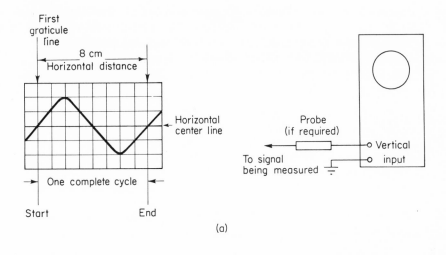

(a)

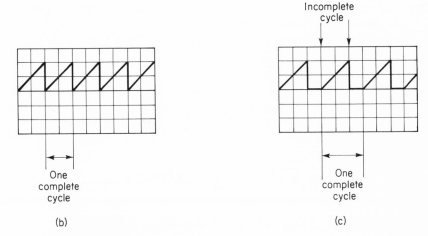

(b)   (c)

Fig. 7-2. Measuring frequency where horizontal sweep is calibrated in relation to time.

4. Connect the probe (if any) to the signal being measured.

5. Switch on the oscilloscope internal recurrent sweep. Set the horizontal sweep control to a sweep rate that will display one complete cycle of the incoming signal (see Fig. 7-2).

NOTE

On most oscilloscopes, it is recommended that the extreme sides of the screen not be used for frequency measurements. There may be some nonlinearity at the beginning and end of the sweep.

6. Adjust the vertical position control so that the beginning and end

points of one complete cycle are located on the horizontal center line.

NOTE

Any two points representing one complete cycle of the waveform can be used. It is usually more convenient to measure one complete cycle at points where the waveform swings from negative to positive (or vice versa), or where the waveform starts its positive (or negative) rise. Figure 7-2 shows some typical examples of a complete cycle for various waveforms.

7. Adjust the horizontal position control to move the selected starting point of the complete cycle to the first graticule line.
8. Measure the horizontal distance between the beginning and end of a complete cycle.

NOTE

If the horizontal sweep is provided with a variable control, make certain it is off or in the calibrate position.

9. Multiply the distance measured in Step 8 by the setting of the horizontal sweep control. If sweep magnification is used, divide the answer by the multiplication factor. Then divide the measured time into 1, or unity, to find the frequency.

Example: Assume that the distance between the beginning and end of a complete cycle is 8 cm (Fig. 7-2a), the horizontal sweep control is set to 0.1 millisecond/cm, and there is no sweep magnification.

Using the equation,

$$\text{time duration} = \frac{\text{horizontal distance(cm)} \times \text{horizontal sweep setting}}{\text{magnification}}$$

Substituting the given values,

$$\text{time duration} = \frac{8 \times 0.1}{1} = 0.8 \text{ millisecond}$$

$$\text{frequency} = \frac{1}{\text{time duration}} = \frac{1}{0.8} = 1250 \text{ Hz}$$

7-3. Frequency and Time Measurements—Shop Oscilloscopes

NOTE

The horizontal sweep circuit of most shop oscilloscopes is provided with controls that are direct reading in relation to frequency. Usually there are two controls: a step selector and a vernier. The sweep frequency of the horizontal trace is equal to the scale settings of the controls. Therefore, when a signal is applied to the vertical input, and the horizontal sweep controls are adjusted until one complete cycle occupies the entire length of the trace, the vertical signal is equal in frequency to the horizontal sweep control scale settings. If desired, the frequency can then be converted to time:

$$\text{time} = \frac{1}{\text{frequency}}$$

1. Connect the equipment as shown in Fig. 7-3.

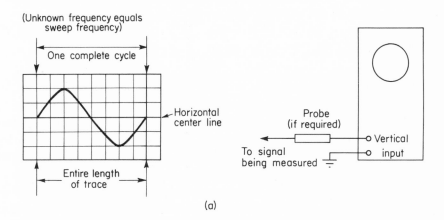

(a)

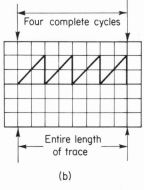

(b)

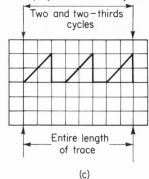

(c)

Fig. 7-3. Measuring frequency where horizontal sweep is calibrated directly in units of frequency.

2. Place the oscilloscope in operation (Chapter 5).
3. Set the vertical step-attenuator to a deflection factor which will allow

the expected signal to be displayed without overdriving the vertical amplifier.

4. Connect the probe (if any) to the signal being measured.
5. Switch on the oscilloscope internal recurrent sweep. Set the horizontal sweep controls (step and vernier) so that one complete cycle occupies the entire length of the trace (Fig. 7-3).
6. Read the unknown vertical signal frequency directly from the horizontal sweep frequency control settings.

Example: Assume that the step horizontal sweep control is set to the 10 kHz position, and that the vernier sweep control indicates 5 (on a total scale of 10). This indicates that the horizontal sweep frequency is 5 kHz. If one complete cycle of vertical signal occupies the entire length of the trace, the vertical signal is also at a frequency of 5 kHz.

7. If it is not practical to display only one cycle on the trace, more than one cycle can be displayed, and the resultant horizontal sweep frequency indication multiplied by the number of cycles. Two important points must be remembered: first, multiply the indicated sweep frequency by the number of cycles appearing on the trace.

Example: Assume that the step horizontal sweep control is set to the 10 kHz position, and the vernier control indicates 5 (on a total scale of 10) when three complete cycles of vertical signal occupy the entire length of the trace. This indicates that the horizontal sweep frequency is 5 kHz, and the vertical signal is at a frequency of three times that amount, or 15 kHz.

Second, it is absolutely essential that an *exact* number of cycles occupy the *entire length* of the trace.

Example: Assume that the step horizontal sweep control is set to the 10 kHz position, and the vernier control indicates 5 (on a total scale of 10) when three and one-third cycles of vertical signal occupy the entire length of the trace. This indicates that the horizontal sweep frequency is 5 kHz, and the vertical signal is at a frequency of three and one-third times that amount, or 16.5 kHz. The exact percentage of the incomplete cycle (one-third) is quite difficult to determine. It is far simpler and more accurate to increase the horizontal sweep frequency until exactly three cycles appear, or decrease the frequency until four cycles occupy the entire length of the trace.

7-4. Frequency Measurements—Lissajous Figures

Lissajous figures or patterns can be used with almost any oscilloscope (shop or laboratory type) and will provide accurate frequency measurements. It must, however, be possible to apply an external signal to the horizontal amplifier, with the internal sweep disabled. Also, an accurately calibrated, variable-frequency signal source must be available to provide a standard frequency.

The use of Lissajous figures to measure frequency involves comparing a signal of unknown frequency (usually applied to the vertical amplifier) against a standard signal of known frequency (usually applied to the horizontal amplifier). The standard frequency is then adjusted until the pattern appears as a circle or ellipse, indicating that both signals are at the same frequency. Where it is not possible to adjust the standard signal frequency to the exact frequency of the unknown signal, the standard is adjusted to a multiple or submultiple. The pattern then appears as a number of stationary loops. The ratio of horizontal loops to vertical loops provides a measure of frequency.

1. Connect the equipment as shown in Fig. 7-4.
2. Place the oscilloscope in operation (Chapter 5).
3. Set the vertical step-attenuator to a deflection factor which will allow the expected signal to be displayed without overdriving the vertical amplifier.
4. Switch off the oscilloscope internal recurrent sweep.
5. Set the gain controls (horizontal and vertical) to spread the pattern over as much of the screen as desired.
6. Set the position controls (horizontal and vertical) until the pattern is centered on the screen.
7. Adjust the standard signal frequency until the pattern stands still. This indicates that the standard signal is at the same frequency as the unknown frequency (if the pattern is a circle or ellipse), or that the standard signal is at a multiple or submultiple of the unknown frequency (if the pattern is composed of stationary loops). If the pattern is still moving (usually spinning), this indicates that the standard signal is not at the same frequency (or multiple) of the unknown frequency. The pattern must be stationary before the frequency can be determined.
8. Note the standard signal frequency. Using this frequency as a basis, observe the Lissajous pattern and compare it against those shown in Fig. 7-4 to determine the unknown frequency.

NOTE

If both signals are sinusoidal and are at the same frequency, the pattern will be a circle (or an ellipse, when the two signals are not exactly in phase) as shown in Fig. 7-4a.

If the standard signal (horizontal) is a multiple of the unknown signal (vertical), the pattern will show more horizontal loops than vertical loops (Fig. 7-4b). For example, if the standard signal frequency is three times that of the unknown signal frequency, there will be three horizontal loops and one vertical loop. If the

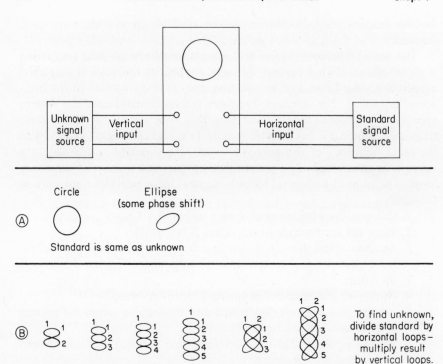

Circle

Ellipse
(some phase shift)

Ⓐ

Standard is same as unknown

Ⓑ

To find unknown,
divide standard by
horizontal loops—
multiply result
by vertical loops.

Standard is multiple of unknown

Ⓒ

Standard is sub—multiple of unknown

To find unknown,
multiply standard
by vertical loops—
divide result
by horizontal
loops.

Fig. 7-4. Measuring frequency with Lissajous patterns.

standard signal frequency were 300 Hz, the unknown signal frequency would be 100 Hz. If there are two vertical loops and three horizontal loops, as another example, the unknown signal frequency would be two-thirds of the standard signal frequency.

If the standard signal (horizontal) is a submultiple of the unknown signal (vertical), the pattern will show more vertical loops than horizontal loops (Fig. 7-4c.) For example, if the standard signal frequency is one-fourth that of the unknown signal frequency, there will be four vertical loops and one horizontal loop. If the standard signal frequency were 100 Hz, the unknown signal frequency would be 400 Hz.

9. If two signals are to be matched, without regard to frequency, it is necessary to adjust only one frequency until the circle (or ellipse) pattern is obtained.

NOTE

It is recommended that the circle pattern be used for all frequency measurements whenever possible. If this is not practical, use the minimum number of loops possible. Note, too, that the use of Lissajous patterns in actual practice is quite difficult and requires considerable skill and practice to make accurate measurements.

7-5. Frequency Measurements—Modulated Ring Pattern

In some cases, it may be difficult to use Lissajous figures, especially when there are many loops to be counted. An alternate method is use of a modulated ring. With the modulated ring method, the display appears as a wheel or gear with a number of teeth. As with Lissajous figures, the modulated ring method requires that an external signal be applied, with the internal sweep disabled, and that the external signal be an accurately calibrated, variable source to provide a standard frequency.

Using the modulated ring method involves comparing a signal of unknown frequency (usually applied to the horizontal amplifier) against the standard signal of known frequency (usually applied through a phase shift network to the vertical amplifier). The standard frequency is then adjusted until the pattern stands still and appears as a circle (or ellipse) with a number of teeth or spikes. The number of teeth indicates the frequency of the unknown signal, when multiplied by the known standard frequency.

It is essential that the unknown frequency be higher than the standard frequency to obtain a proper pattern. Also, it must be possible to increase the amplitude of the known signal above that of the unknown signal, to prevent distortion of the pattern.

1. Connect the equipment as shown in Fig. 7-5.

NOTE

The phase shift required to produce the circle (or ellipse) pattern is composed of variable resistance R_1 and fixed capacitor C_1. To obtain the correct voltage to produce a good circle, the resistance

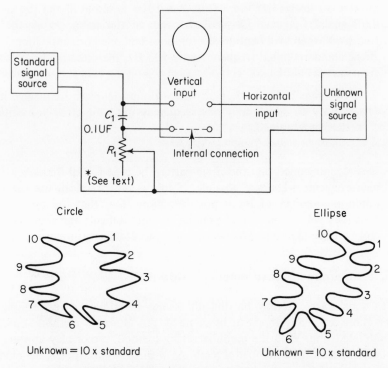

Fig. 7-5. Measuring frequency with modulated ring pattern.

of R_1 should be equal to the reactance of C_1 at the operating frequency of the known signal source. By making R_1 variable, it is possible to match the change in C_1 reactance over a wide range of standard signal frequencies.

2. Place the oscilloscope in operation (Chapter 5).
3. Set the step-attenuators to deflection factors which will allow the expected signals to be displayed without overdriving the amplifiers.
4. Switch off the oscilloscope internal recurrent sweep.
5. Temporarily remove the unknown signal source.
6. Set the position controls (horizontal and vertical) until the pattern is centered on the screen.
7. Adjust R_1 for a ring pattern.
8. Set the gain controls (horizontal and vertical) to spread the pattern over as much of the screen as desired.
9. Switch on the unknown signal source, and note that the ring pattern becomes modulated (teeth or spikes appear). It may be necessary to readjust the horizontal gain to produce a readable pattern.
10. Adjust the standard signal frequency until the pattern stands still.

This indicates that the unknown signal is at a multiple of the known signal frequency. The pattern must be stationary before the frequency can be determined.

11. Note the standard signal frequency. Using this frequency as a basis, observe the number of teeth appearing on the ring and determine the unknown frequency.

Example: Assume that the standard signal frequency is 1 kHz, and there are 7 teeth appearing on the ring.

The unknown signal frequency is 7 kHz.

$$1 \text{ kHz} \times 7 = 7 \text{ kHz}$$

7-6. Frequency Measurements—Broken Ring Pattern

The broken ring pattern is similar to the modulated ring pattern described in Sec. 7-5. Both are alternate methods to the use of Lissajous figures for frequency measurement. With the broken ring method, the display appears as a ring broken into segments. As with the modulated ring method, the broken ring method requires that an external signal be applied, with the internal sweep disabled, and that the external signal be an accurately calibrated, variable source to provide standard frequency.

The broken-ring method has an additional requirement in that the oscilloscope must be capable of Z-axis (intensity) modulation.

Use of the broken-ring method involves comparing a signal of unknown frequency (applied to the Z axis) against the standard signal of known frequency (applied to the vertical and horizontal amplifiers through a phase-shift network). The standard frequency is then adjusted until the pattern stands still and appears as a circle (or ellipse) with a number of bright traces and blanks. The bright traces or segments are made by the positive half-cycles of the unknown signal applied to the Z axis, whereas the blanks are made by the negative half-cycles.

The number of segments (or blanks, whichever are easier to read) indicate the frequency of the unknown signal, when multiplied by the known standard frequency. It is essential that the unknown frequency be higher than the standard frequency to obtain a proper pattern.

The broken-ring method is superior to the modulated-ring method in that it is usually easier to distinguish blanks or traces than teeth in the ring pattern. Except for this, the accuracy of both methods is the same.

1. Connect the equipment as shown in Fig. 7-6.

NOTE

The phase shift required to produce the circle (or ellipse) pattern is composed of variable resistance R_1 and fixed capacitor C_1. To

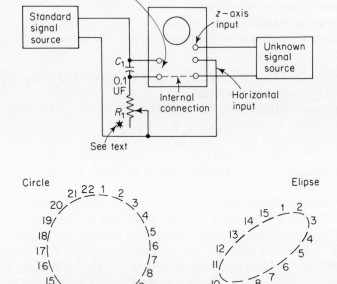

Fig. 7-6. Measuring frequency with broken ring pattern.

obtain the correct voltage to produce a good circle, the resistance
of R_1 should be equal to the reactance of C_1 at the operating
frequency of the known signal source. By making R_1 variable, it
is possible to match the change in C_1 reactance over a wide range
of standard signal frequencies.

2. Place the oscilloscope in operation (Chapter 5).
3. Set the step-attenuators to deflection factors which will allow the
   expected signals to be displayed without overdriving the amplifiers.
4. Switch off the oscilloscope internal recurrent sweep.
5. Temporarily remove the unknown signal source.
6. Set the position controls (horizontal and vertical) until the pattern
   is centered on the screen.
7. Adjust R_1 for a ring pattern on the screen.
8. Set the gain controls (horizontal and vertical) to spread the pattern
   over as much of the screen as desired.
9. Switch on the unknown signal source and note that the ring pattern
   is broken into segments.

10. Adjust the standard signal frequency until the pattern stands still. This indicates that the unknown signal is at a multiple of the known signal frequency. The pattern must be stationary before the frequency can be determined.
11. Note the standard signal frequency. Using this frequency as a basis, observe the number of segments (or blanks, whichever is most convenient to read) appearing on the ring and determine the unknown frequency.

Example: Assume that the standard signal frequency is 1 kHz, and there are 14 segments (or blanks) appearing on the ring.
The unknown signal frequency is 14 kHz.

$$1 \text{ kHz} \times 14 = 14 \text{ kHz}$$

7-7. Frequency Measurements—Broken-Line Pattern

The broken-line pattern is similar to the broken ring pattern described in Sec. 7-6. Both are alternate methods to the use of Lissajous figures for frequency measurement. With the broken-line method, the display appears as a straight horizontal line (the vertical deflection is not used) broken into segments. As with the broken-ring method, the broken-line method requires that an external signal be applied, with the internal sweep disabled and that the external signal be an accurately calibrated, variable source to provide a standard frequency.

The broken-line method requires that the oscilloscope be capable of Z-axis (intensity) modulation, but does not require a phase-shift network.

Use of the broken-line method involves comparing a signal of unknown frequency (applied to the Z axis) against the standard signal of known frequency (applied to the horizontal amplifier). The standard frequency is then adjusted until the pattern stands still and appears as a straight line with a number of bright traces and blanks. The bright traces or segments are made by the positive half-cycles of the unknown signal applied to the Z axis, whereas the blanks are made by the negative half-cycles.

The number of segments (or blanks, whichever are easier to read) indicates the frequency of the unknown signal, when multiplied by the known standard frequency. It is essential that the unknown frequency be higher than the standard frequency to obtain a proper pattern.

The broken-line method is superior to the broken-ring method because it is simpler and does not require a phase-shift network, but the broken-line method does not permit as high a count as the broken-ring method.

1. Connect the equipment as shown in Fig. 7-7.
2. Place the oscilloscope in operation (Chapter 5).
3. Set the horizontal step-attenuator to a deflection factor which will

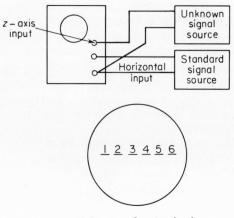

Unknown = 6 x standard

Fig. 7-7. Measuring frequency with broken-line pattern.

allow the expected signals to be displayed without overdriving the horizontal amplifier.

4. Switch off the oscilloscope internal recurrent sweep.
5. Temporarily remove the unknown signal source.
6. Set the position controls (horizontal and vertical) until the pattern is centered on the screen.
7. Set the horizontal gain control to spread the pattern over as much of the screen as desired.
8. Switch on the unknown signal source and note that the horizontal line is broken into segments.
9. Adjust the standard signal frequency until the pattern stands still. This indicates that the unknown signal is at a multiple of the known signal frequency. The pattern must be stationary before the frequency can be determined.
10. Note the standard signal frequency. Using this frequency as a basis, observe the number of segments (or blanks, whichever is most convenient to read) appearing on the horizontal line, and determine the unknown frequency.

Example: Assume that the standard signal frequency is 1 kHz, and there are 5 segments (or blanks) appearing on the line.

The unknown frequency is 5 kHz.

$$1 \text{ kHz} \times 5 = 5 \text{ kHz}$$

7-8. Phase Measurements—Dual-trace Method

The dual-trace method of phase measurement provides a high degree of accuracy at all frequencies, but is especially useful at frequencies above

100 kHz where X-Y phase measurements (Sec. 7-9) may prove inaccurate owing to inherent internal phase shift.

The dual-trace method also has the advantage of measuring phase difference between signals of different amplitudes, frequency, and waveshape. The method can be applied directly to those oscilloscopes having a built-in dual-trace feature, or to a conventional single-trace oscilloscope using an electronic switch or "chopper" (Chapter 4). Either way, the procedure consists essentially of displaying both traces on the oscilloscope screen simultaneously, measuring the distance (in scale divisions) between related points on the two traces, and then converting this distance into phase.

1. Connect the equipment as shown in Fig. 7-8.

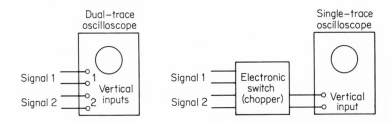

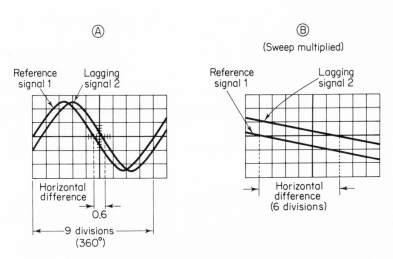

Fig. 7-8. Measuring phase difference with dual traces.

2. Place the oscilloscope in operation (Chapter 5).

NOTE

For the most accurate results, the cables connecting the two signals to the oscilloscope input should be of the same length and characteristics. At higher frequencies, a difference in cable length or characteristics could introduce a phase shift.

3. Set the step-attenuators to deflection factors which will allow the expected signals to be displayed without overdriving the amplifiers.
4. Switch on the oscilloscope internal recurrent sweep.
5. Set the position controls (horizontal and vertical) until the pattern is centered on the screen.
6. Set the gain controls (horizontal and vertical) to spread the patterns over as much of the screen as desired.
7. Switch on the dual-trace function of the oscilloscope, or switch on the electronic "chopper."
8. Adjust the sweep controls until one cycle of the reference signal occupies exactly nine divisions (9 cm horizontally) of the screen.

NOTE

Either of the two signals can be used as the reference signal, unless otherwise specified by requirements of the particular test. It is usually simpler if the signal of the lowest frequency is used as the reference signal.

9. Determine the phase factor of the reference signal.

Example: If 9 cm represents one complete cycle, or 360°, then 1 cm represents 40° (360° ÷ 9 divisions (cm) = 40°/cm).

10. Measure the horizontal distance between corresponding points on the waveform. Multiply the measured distance (in centimeters) by 40° (phase factor) to obtain the exact amount of phase difference.

Example: Assume a horizontal difference of 0.6 cm with a phase factor of 40° as shown in Fig. 7-8a.

Using the equation,

$$\text{phase difference} = \begin{array}{c}\text{horizontal} \\ \text{difference} \\ \text{(in cm)}\end{array} \times \begin{array}{c}\text{phase} \\ \text{factor}\end{array}$$

Substituting the given values,

$$\text{phase difference} = 0.6 \times 40°$$

The phase difference would be 24°.

11. If the oscilloscope is provided with a sweep magnification control where the sweep rate is increased by some fixed amount (5X, 10X, etc.), and only a portion of one cycle can be displayed, more accurate phase measurements can be made. In this case, the phase factor is determined as described in Step 9. Then the approximate phase difference is determined as described in Step 10. Without changing

any other controls, the sweep rate is increased (by the sweep magnification control or the sweep rate control) and a new horizontal distance measurement is made, as shown in Fig. 7-8b.

Example: If the sweep rate were increased 10 times (with the magnifier or sweep rate control), the adjusted phase factor would be $40° \div 10 = 4°/cm$. Figure 7-8b shows the same signal as used in Fig. 7-8a, but the sweep rate set to X10. With a horizontal difference of 6 cm, the phase difference would be

$$\text{phase difference} = \begin{matrix} \text{horizontal} \\ \text{difference} \\ \text{(in cm)} \end{matrix} \times \begin{matrix} \text{adjusted} \\ \text{phase} \\ \text{factor} \end{matrix}$$

Substituting the given values,

$$\text{phase difference} = 6 \times 4°$$

The phase difference would be 24°.

7-9. Phase Measurements—X-Y Method

The *X-Y* phase measurement method can be used to measure the phase difference between two sine-wave signals of the *same frequency*. This method provides a method of measurement for signal frequencies up to about 100 kHz more precise than the dual-trace method discussed in Sec. 7-8. Above this frequency, however, the inherent phase difference between the horizontal and vertical systems makes accurate phase measurement difficult. Therefore, the *X-Y* method should be limited to phase measurement of lower-frequency signals and to signals of the same frequency.

In the *X-Y* method, one of the sine-wave signals provides horizontal deflection (*X*), and the other provides the vertical deflection (*Y*). The phase angle between the two signals can be determined from the resulting Lissajous pattern.

1. Connect the equipment as shown in Fig. 7-9a.

NOTE

Figure 7-9a shows the test connection necessary to determine the inherent phase shift (if any) between the horizontal and vertical deflection systems of the oscilloscope. Even the most expensive laboratory oscilloscopes with identical horizontal and vertical amplifiers will have some inherent phase shift, particularly at the higher frequencies. Therefore, all oscilloscopes should be checked and the inherent phase shift recorded before any phase measurements are made. Inherent phase shift also should be checked periodically. If there is excessive phase shift (in relation to the

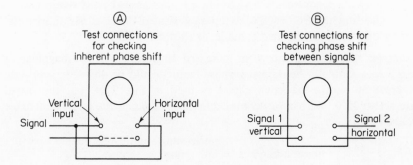

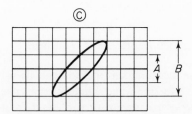

Fig. 7-9. Measuring phase difference with X-Y method.

anticipated phase shift of signals to be measured), the oscilloscope should not be used. A possible exception exists when the signals to be measured are of sufficient amplitude to be applied directly to the oscilloscope deflection plates, and thus bypass the horizontal and vertical amplifiers.

2. Place the oscilloscope in operation (Chapter 5).
3. Set the step-attenuators to deflection factors which will allow the expected signals to be displayed without overdriving the amplifiers.
4. Switch off the oscilloscope internal recurrent sweep.
5. Set the gain controls (horizontal and vertical) to spread the pattern over as much of the screen as desired.
6. Set the position controls (horizontal and vertical) until the pattern is centered on the screen. Center the display in relation to the vertical graticule line. Measure distance A and B, as shown in Fig. 7-9c. Distance A is the vertical measurement between the two points where the trace crosses the vertical center line. Distance B is the maximum vertical height of the display.
7. Divide A by B to obtain the sine of the phase angle between the two signals. The angle can then be obtained from Table 7-1. The resultant angle is the inherent phase shift.

TABLE 7-1.

Table of Sines

Sine	Angle	Sine	Angle
0.0000	0	.7193	46
.0175	1	.7314	47
.0349	2	.7431	48
.0523	3	.7547	49
.0689	4	.7660	50
.0872	5	.7771	51
.1045	6	.7880	52
.1219	7	.7986	53
.1392	8	.8090	54
.1564	9	.8192	55
.1736	10	.8290	56
.1908	11	.8387	57
.2079	12	.8480	58
.2250	13	.8572	59
.2419	14	.8660	60
.2588	15	.8746	61
.2756	16	.8829	62
.2924	17	.8910	63
.3090	18	.8988	64
.3256	19	.9063	65
.3420	20	.9135	66
.3584	21	.9205	67
.3746	22	.9272	68
.3907	23	.9336	69
.4067	24	.9397	70
.4226	25	.9455	71
.4384	26	.9511	72
.4540	27	.9563	73
.4695	28	.9613	74
.4848	29	.9659	75
.5000	30	.9703	76
.5150	31	.9744	77
.5299	32	.9781	78
.5446	33	.9816	79
.5592	34	.9848	80
.5736	35	.9877	81
.5878	36	.9903	82
.6018	37	.9925	83
.6157	38	.9945	84
.6293	39	.9962	85
.6428	40	.9976	86
.6561	41	.9986	87
.6691	42	.9994	88
.6820	43	.9998	89
.6947	44	1.0000	90
.7071	45		

NOTE

If the display appears as a diagonal straight line, the two amplifiers are either in phase (tilted upper right to lower left) or 180° out of phase (tilted upper left to lower right). If the display is a circle, the signals are 90° out of phase. Figure 7-10 shows the Lissajous displays produced between 0° and 360°. Notice that above 180° phase shift, the resultant display will be the same as at some lower frequency. Therefore, it may be difficult to tell whether the signal is

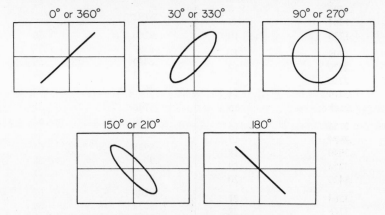

Fig. 7-10. Phase of typical X-Y displays.

leading or lagging. One way to determine correct phase (leading or lagging) is to introduce a small, known phase shift to one of the inputs. The proper angle may then be determined by noting the direction in which the pattern changes.

8. Once the inherent phase shift has been determined, connect the equipment as shown in Fig. 7-9b. Repeat Steps 3–7 to find the phase angle between the two signals.

9. Subtract the inherent phase difference from the phase angle to determine the true phase difference.

Example: Assume an inherent phase difference of 2°, with a display as shown in Fig. 7-9c, where A is 2 cm and B is 4 cm.

Using the equation,

$$\text{sine of phase angle} = \frac{A}{B}$$

Substituting the given values,

$$\text{sine of phase angle} = \frac{2}{4} = 0.5$$

From Table 7-1,

$$\text{sine of phase angle} = 30°$$

To adjust for the phase difference between X and Y amplifiers, subtract the inherent phase factor

$$\begin{array}{l}\text{actual} \\ \text{phase} \\ \text{factor}\end{array} = \text{sine of phase angle} - \begin{array}{l}\text{inherent} \\ \text{phase} \\ \text{difference}\end{array}$$

Substituting the given values,

$$\begin{array}{l}\text{actual} \\ \text{phase} \\ \text{factor}\end{array} = 30° - 2° = 28°$$

7-10. Phase Measurements between Voltage and Current

It is sometimes necessary to measure the phase difference between a voltage and current applied across the same load. This can be accomplished passing a portion of the current through a fixed resistor, thus converting the current to a voltage. The phase of the resultant voltage is then compared to the load voltage phase. A resistor, capable of the necessary wattage dissipation, is the only other component required for the procedure. Either the X-Y method or the dual-trace method can be used for the actual phase comparison.

Figure 7-11 shows the test connections required for converting the current into a voltage and applying both voltages to the oscilloscope.

In Fig. 7-11a, the signal voltage E_1 is applied across the load and test resistor R_1. Voltage E_1 is also applied to one of the vertical inputs. The current-developed voltage E_2 appears across R_1, and is applied to the other vertical input.

In Fig. 7-11b, the signal voltage E_1 is applied across the load and test resistor R_1. Voltage E_1 is also applied to the electronic switch (chopper). The current-developed voltage E_2 appears across R_1 and is applied to the other electronic switch input.

In Fig. 7-11c, the signal voltage E_1 is applied across the load and test resistor R_1. Voltage E_1 is also applied to the vertical input. The current-developed voltage E_2 appears across R_1 and is applied to the horizontal input.

Once the test connections have been made, the phase difference between voltage and current can be determined by the procedures of Sec. 7-8 (dual-trace), or Sec. 7-9 (X-Y method), whichever applies.

NOTE

The actual resistance value of R_1 is not critical. It should be low in comparison to the resistance value of the load. Usually 1–10 ohms is adequate to develop sufficient voltage for measurement. The wattage of the resistor R_1 must be at least double the square of

(a) Dual trace method (dual trace oscilloscope)

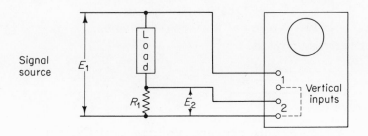

(b) Dual trace method (electronic switch)

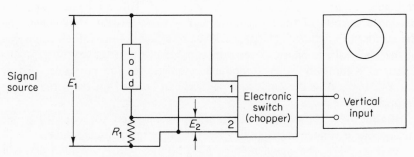

(c) x−y method

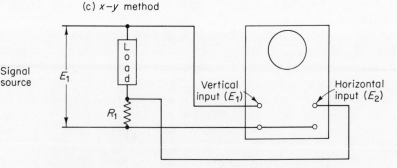

Fig. 7-11. Phase measurement between voltage and current.

the maximum current (in amperes). For example, if the maximum anticipated current is 10 amp, the minimum wattage of the resistor should be $10^2 \times 2 = 200$ watts.

7-11. Phase Measurements between Two Currents

It is sometimes necessary to measure the phase difference between two currents. This can be accomplished by passing the currents through fixed

(a) Dual trace method (dual trace oscilloscope)

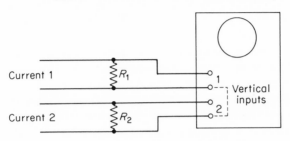

(b) Dual trace method (electronic switch)

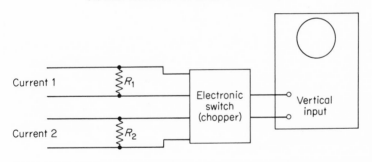

(c) x–y method

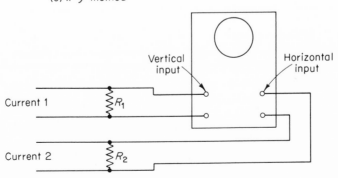

Fig. 7-12. Phase measurements between currents.

resistors, thus converting the currents into voltages. The phase of the resultant voltages is then compared. Two resistors, capable of the necessary wattage dissipation, are the only other components required for the procedure. Either the X-Y or the dual-trace method can be used for the actual phase comparison.

Figure 7-12 shows the test connections required for converting the currents into voltages and applying both voltages to the oscilloscope.

In Fig. 7-12a, the currents are applied across corresponding resistors R_1 and R_2, with the resulting voltages applied to the two corresponding vertical inputs.

In Fig. 7-12b, the currents are applied across corresponding resistors R_1 and R_2, with the resulting voltages applied to the two corresponding electronic switch inputs.

In Fig. 7-12c, the currents are applied across corresponding resistors R_1 and R_2, with the resulting voltages applied to the vertical and horizontal inputs.

Once the test connections have been made, the phase difference between the two currents can be determined by the procedures of Sec. 7-8 (dual-trace) or Sec. 7-9 (X-Y method), whichever applies.

NOTE

The actual resistance value of R_1 is not critical. It should, however, be low in comparison to the load. Usually 1–10 ohms is adequate to develop sufficient voltage for measurement. The wattage of each resistor must be at least double the square of the maximum current (in amperes). For example, if the maximum anticipated current is 10 amp, the minimum wattage of the resistor should be $10^2 \times 2 = 200$ watts.

CHAPTER 8

Using Oscilloscopes
with Sweep Generators

The prime function of a sweep generator is the sweep frequency alignment of TV and FM receivers. In this application, sweep generators are used with oscilloscopes to display the bandpass characteristics of the receiver under test. The sweep generator/oscilloscope combination can also be used effectively to check the operation of filters, to check impedance of such items as transmission lines, antennas, and tuning stubs, and to determine impedance match.

A sweep generator is an FM generator. When a sweep generator is set to a given frequency, this is center frequency. In essence, a sweep generator is a frequency-modulated radio-frequency generator. The usual frequency modulation rate is 60 Hz for most TV and FM sweep generators. Other sweep rates could be used, but since power lines usually have a 60 Hz frequency, this frequency is both convenient and economical for the sweep rate.

Some sweep generators incorporate a marker generator. Marker signals are necessary to pinpoint frequencies when making sweep frequency alignments and tests. Although sweep generators are accurate in both center frequency and sweep width, it is almost impossible to pick out a particular frequency along the spectrum of frequencies being swept. Therefore, fixed frequency "marker" signals are injected into the circuit along with the sweep frequency generator output. On sweep generators without a built-in marker generator, markers can be added by means of an absorption-type marker adder. These marker adders can be built in, or they are available as accessories. Where a marker adder would provide too limited a number of fixed frequency points, a marker generator can be used in conjunction with a sweep generator and an oscilloscope. Basically, a marker generator is an RF signal generator which has highly accurate dial markings, and which can be calibrated precisely against internal or external signals. The sweep generator is tuned to sweep the band of frequencies passed by the wideband circuits (tuner, i-f, video, filter, etc.), and a trace representing the response characteristics of the circuits is displayed on the oscilloscope. The marker generator is used to provide calibrated markers along the response curve. When the marker signal from the marker generator is coupled into the test circuit, a vertical "pip," or marker, appears on the curve. When the marker generator is tuned to a frequency within the passband accepted by the equipment under test, the marker indicates the position of that frequency on the sweep trace.

Another feature found on some sweep generators is a blanking circuit. When the sweep generator output is swept across its spectrum, the frequencies go from low to high, then return from high to low. With the blanking circuit actuated, the return or retrace is blanked off. This makes it possible to view a zero-reference line on the oscilloscope during the retrace period.

8-1. Basic Sweep Generator/Oscilloscope Test Procedure

The following steps describe the *basic* procedure for using a sweep generator with an oscilloscope. Later sections in this chapter describe procedures for using the sweep generator/oscilloscope combination to test specific equipment or circuits.

1. Connect the equipment as shown in Fig. 8-1.
2. Place the oscilloscope in operation (Chapter 5).
3. Place the sweep generator in operation as described in its instruction manual.
4. Switch off the oscilloscope internal recurrent sweep.
5. Set the oscilloscope sweep selector and sync selector to external. Under these conditions, the oscilloscope horizontal sweep should be obtained from the generator sweep output, and the length of the horizontal sweep should represent total sweep spectrum. For example, if the sweep is from 10 to 20 kHz, the left-hand end of the horizontal trace represents 10 kHz and the right-hand end represents 20 kHz. Any point along the horizontal trace will represent a corresponding frequency. For example, the midpoint on the trace would represent 15 kHz. If a rough approximation of frequency is desired, the horizontal gain control can be adjusted until the trace occupies an exact number of scale divisions, such as 10 cm for the 10–20 kHz

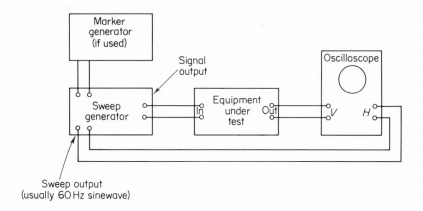

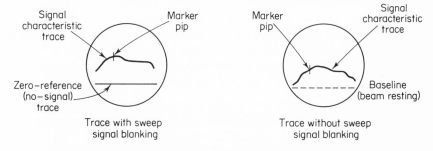

Fig. 8-1. Basic sweep generator/oscilloscope test connections.

sweep signal. Each centimeter division would then represent 1 kHz.

6. If a more accurate frequency measurement is desired, the marker generator must be used. The marker generator output frequency is adjusted until the marker pip is aligned at the desired point on the trace. The frequency is then read from the marker generator frequency dial.

7. The response curve (trace) depends upon the device under test. If the device has a passband (as do most receiver circuits) and the sweep generator is set so that its sweep is wider than the passband, the trace will start low at the left, rise toward the middle, and then drop off at the right, as shown in Fig. 8-1. The sweep generator/oscilloscope method will tell at a glance the overall passband characteristics of the device (sharp response, flat response, irregular response at certain frequencies, etc.). The exact frequency limits of the passband can be measured with the marker generator pip.

8. Switch the sweep generator blanking control on or off as desired. Some sweep generators do not have a blanking function. With the blanking function in effect, there will be a zero-reference line on the

trace. With the blanking function off, the horizontal baseline will not appear. The sweep generator blanking function is not to be confused with the oscilloscope blanking (which is bypassed when the sweep signal is applied directly to the horizontal amplifier).

8-2. Checking Sweep Generator Output Uniformity

Many sweep generators do not have a uniform output. That is, the output voltage is not constant over the swept band. In some tests, this can lead to false conclusions. In other tests, it is only necessary to know the amount of nonuniformity, and then make allowances. For example, a sweep generator can be checked for flatness before connection to a circuit, and any variation in output noted. If the output remains the same after it is connected to the circuit, even though it may have variations, the circuit under test is not at fault. Sweep generator output can be checked as follows:

1. Connect the equipment as shown in Fig. 8-2.

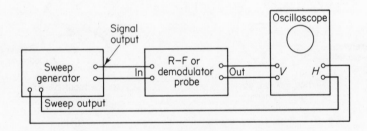

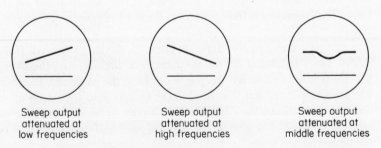

Fig. 8-2. Checking sweep generator output uniformity.

NOTE

The RF or demodulator probe shown in Fig. 8-2 can be omitted if the sweep generator output signal frequency is within the pass-

band of the oscilloscope vertical amplifier. This is not usually the
case with shop-type oscilloscopes, so some form of demodulator
is necessary. If the oscilloscope is not equipped with a demodulator
or RF probe, demodulator networks can be fabricated as shown
in Fig. 8-3. Figure 8-3a is for a single-ended sweep generator
output; Fig. 8-3b is for a double-ended or balanced output. The

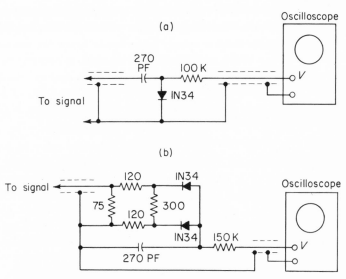

Fig. 8-3. R-F demodulator probe circuits.

balanced output is often found on sweep generators designed
specifically for use with TV and FM receivers.

2. Place the oscilloscope in operation (Chapter 5).
3. Place the sweep generator in operation as described in its instruction
   manual. Set sweep width to maximum.
4. Switch off the oscilloscope internal recurrent sweep.
5. Set the oscilloscope sweep selector and sync selector to external so
   that the horizontal sweep is obtained from the generator sweep
   output.
6. Switch the sweep generator blanking control on or off as desired.
   With the blanking function not in effect, only one trace will appear.
   This should be deflected vertically from the normal trace resting
   position. With the blanking function on, there will be two traces.
   The upper trace is the generator output characteristic; the lower
   trace is the no-signal trace.
7. Check the sweep generator output trace for flatness. If the right-hand
   side of the trace drops or slopes, this indicates that the sweep output

is reduced at the high-frequency end of the sweep. A slope to the left indicates a reduced output at the low-frequency end of the sweep. If the trace drops off suddenly, or dips in the middle, this indicates an uneven output. A perfectly flat trace or (more realistically) a trace that has only a slight curvature at the ends indicates an even output across the entire swept band.

8. Leave the sweep width at maximum, but adjust the center frequency of the sweep generator over its entire range. Check that the output is flat, or at least that any variations are consistent, across the range of the sweep generator.

8-3. Alternate Sweep Generator Operation

The procedures described in this chapter can be performed with the oscilloscope sweep selector set to internal, and the sync selector set to line. Two conditions must be met. First, the sweep generator must be swept at the line frequency. Second, the oscilloscope, or sweep generator, must have a phasing control so that the two sweeps can be synchronized. The phasing problem is discussed in Sec. 2-3. This alternate method is used where the sweep generator does not have a sweep output separate from the signal output, or when it is not desired to use the sweep output. Blanking of the trace (if any blanking is used) is controlled by the oscilloscope circuits.

8-4. Measuring Transmission Line Impedance

The sweep generator/oscilloscope combination can be used to measure the impedance of transmission lines, TV antenna lead-in wire, or cables. This method is particularly effective since it provides an impedance check over a broad frequency range.

1. Connect the equipment as shown in Fig. 8-4.
2. Place the oscilloscope in operation (Chapter 5). Switch off internal recurrent sweep. Set the oscilloscope sweep selector and sync selector to external.
3. Place the sweep generator in operation as described in its instruction manual. Switch sweep generator blanking control on or off as desired. Tune the sweep generator to the normal operating frequency with which the transmission line is to be used. Adjust the sweep width to cover the complete range of frequencies.
4. Adjust the variable resistance to the supposed impedance value of the transmission line.
5. The oscilloscope pattern should show a flat trace. If not, adjust the variable resistance until the trace is flat.

6. Disconnect the variable resistance (without disturbing its setting) and measure the resistance with an ohmmeter. This value is equal to the transmission line characteristic impedance.

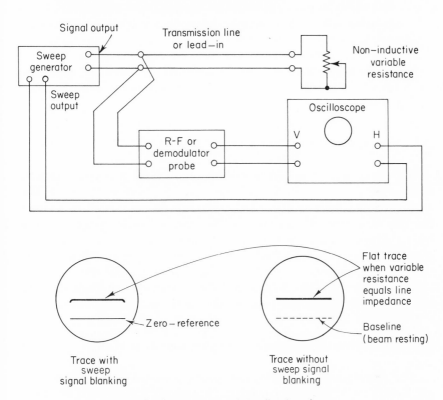

Fig. 8-4. Measuring transmission line impedance.

7. If the trace cannot be made flat, temporarily disconnect the transmission line but leave the sweep generator output connected to the oscilloscope. Check the trace pattern. If it is still not flat, the sweep generator output is not uniform. (Refer to Sec. 8-2).

8-5. Measuring Impedance Match

The sweep generator/oscilloscope combination can be used to measure impedance match between a transmission line and antenna or any other terminating device. This method provides a check of impedance match over a broad frequency range.

1. Connect the equipment as shown in Fig. 8-5.
2. Place the oscilloscope in operation (Chapter 5). Switch off internal

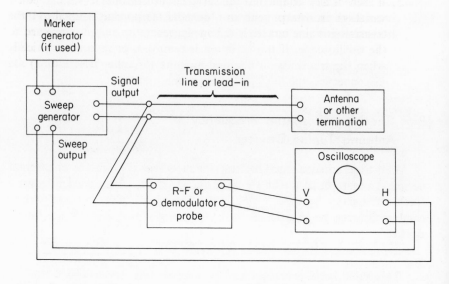

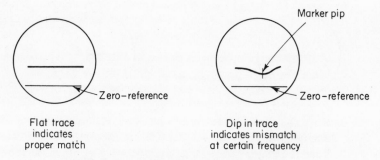

Fig. 8-5. Measuring impedance match.

recurrent sweep. Set the oscilloscope sweep selector and sync selector to external.

3. Place the sweep generator in operation as described in its instruction manual. Switch sweep generator blanking control on or off as desired. Tune the sweep generator to the normal operating frequency with which the transmission line and antenna (or other terminating device) are to be used. Adjust the sweep width to cover the complete range of frequencies.

4. If the transmission line and antenna are properly matched, the oscilloscope will show a flat trace. If the oscilloscope trace is not flat, and it is desired to determine the frequency at which the mismatch occurs, the marker generator can be adjusted until the marker pip is aligned at the desired point on the trace. The mismatch frequency, or band of frequencies, can be read from the marker generator frequency dial.

5. If there is any doubt that the variation in trace flatness is caused by variation in sweep generator output, temporarily disconnect the transmission line but leave the sweep generator output connected to the oscilloscope. If the variation is removed, or reduced drastically when the transmission line and antenna (or other termination) are disconnected, this indicates a mismatch.

8-6. Checking Resonant Frequency of Antenna Tuning Devices

Many times antennas used with transmission lines are tuned by an external device. An example of this is TV antennas which are often tuned to cover a specific frequency by means of a stub. The sweep generator/oscilloscope combination can be used to measure the resonant frequency of the tuning device.

NOTE

This same basic procedure can be used to tune (or to check the resonant frequency) of any resonant circuit. It is essential, however, that the sweep generator output be at the fundamental frequency of the resonant circuit for accurate results.

1. Connect the equipment as shown in Fig. 8-6.
2. Place the oscilloscope in operation (Chapter 5). Switch off internal recurrent sweep. Set the oscilloscope sweep selector and sync selector to external.
3. Place the sweep generator in operation as described in its instruction manual. Switch sweep generator blanking control on or off as desired. Tune the sweep generator to the frequency at which the tuning device is supposed to be resonant. Adjust the sweep width to cover a wide range of frequencies, but not so wide that the nearest harmonic is covered. If harmonics are covered, their indications on the trace may prove confusing.
4. Note the point on the trace at which the dip occurs. The dip indicates the frequency of the resonant circuit or tuning device.
5. The procedure can be reversed to adjust the tuning device to a given frequency, if desired.
6. For greatest accuracy, adjust the marker generator until the marker pip is aligned at the center of the trace dip. The exact resonant frequency can then be read from the marker generator frequency dial.

NOTE

The dip characteristics indicate the sharpness or Q of the tuning device or resonant circuit. A broad dip indicates a low Q; a sharp dip indicates a high Q.

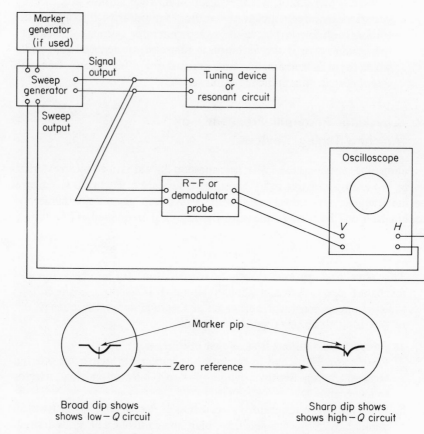

Fig. 8-6. Checking resonant frequency of antenna tuning devices.

8-7. Checking Devices Inserted in Transmission Lines

When any device is inserted in a transmission line, there occurs a possibility of mismatch between the line and the device. This will produce attenuation at certain frequencies. Even if there is no mismatch, the device (such as a coupler, splitter, pick-off probe), can produce some attenuation at all frequencies. The sweep generator/oscilloscope combination can be used to check impedance match and attenuation of any device inserted into a transmission line.

1. Connect the equipment as shown in Fig. 8-7.
2. Place the oscilloscope in operation (Chapter 5). Switch off internal recurrent sweep. Set the oscilloscope sweep selector and sync selector to external.
3. Place the sweep generator in operation as described in its instruction

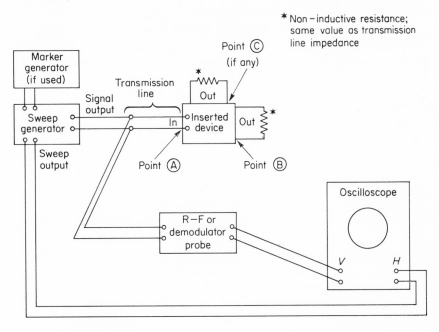

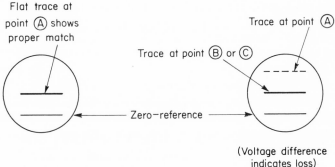

Fig. 8-7. Checking devices inserted in transmission lines.

manual. Switch sweep generator blanking control on or off as desired. Tune the sweep generator to the normal operating frequency with which the transmission line and inserted device are to be used. Adjust the sweep width to cover the complete range of frequencies.

4. With the probe connected at the sweep generator output, the oscilloscope will show a flat trace if the transmission line and inserted device are properly matched. If the trace is not flat, and it is desired to determine the frequency at which the mismatch occurs, the marker generator can be adjusted until the marker pip is aligned at the desired

point on the trace. The mismatch frequency, or band of frequencies, can be read from the marker generator frequency dial.

5. If there is any doubt that the variation in trace flatness is caused by variation in sweep generator output, temporarily disconnect the transmission line, but leave the oscilloscope probe connected to the sweep generator output. If the variation is removed, or drastically reduced when the transmission line and inserted device are disconnected, this indicates a mismatch.

6. Once the match or mismatch has been established, connect the probe to the inserted device input at point A (Fig. 8-7). This will establish a vertical reference deflection. Then, connect the probe to point B, and to point C (if any) in turn.

7. The oscilloscope vertical deflection should be lower at points B and C than at point A because almost any device inserted into a transmission line will show some loss or attenuation. Unless there is some special design characteristic, the output at points B and C should be the same. The voltage difference between the signal at points A and B (or A and C) can be measured directly on the oscilloscope (assuming that the vertical system is voltage calibrated) and converted to a ratio, decibel value, or whatever is desired.

8-8. Measuring Input and Output Impedances

The input and output impedances of RF (and audio) components can be checked quickly and over a broad range of frequencies with the sweep generator/oscilloscope combination.

1. Connect the equipment as shown in Fig. 8-8.

2. Place the oscilloscope in operation (Chapter 5). Switch off internal recurrent sweep. Set the oscilloscope sweep selector and sync selector to external.

3. Place the sweep generator in operation as described in its instruction manual. Switch sweep generator blanking control on or off as desired. Tune the sweep generator to the normal operating frequency with which the component is to be used. Adjust the sweep width to cover the complete range of frequencies.

4. Disconnect resistors R_1 and R_2 from the circuit.

5. Adjust the sweep generator output level so that the trace is at a convenient vertical scale marking. Note this vertical deflection scale marking.

6. Connect resistor R_1 back into the circuit. Vary the resistance of R_1 until the voltage indicated on the oscilloscope is one-half the original value.

7. Disconnect resistor R_1 from the circuit, and measure its d-c resistance.

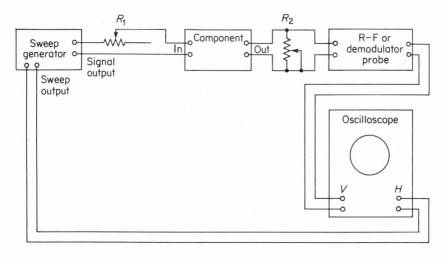

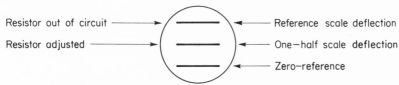

Fig. 8-8. Measuring input and output impedances.

This resistance is equivalent to the input impedance of the component.

8. With both R_1 and R_2 out of the circuit, again adjust the sweep generator output level so that the trace is at a convenient vertical scale indication.

9. Connect resistor R_2 back into the circuit. Vary the resistance of R_2 until the voltage indication on the oscilloscope is one-half the original value.

10. Disconnect resistor R_2 from the circuit and measure its d-c resistance. This resistance is equivalent to the output impedance of the component.

NOTE

This method is accurate if the impedance to be measured is *resistive*, but only approximate if the impedance is reactive.

8-9. Measuring Input Impedance

Many RF components have an input circuit, but no measurable output. An antenna is a good example of such a component. The input impedance of these components can be measured quickly and over a broad range of frequencies with the sweep generator/oscilloscope combination.

1. Connect the equipment as shown in Fig. 8-9.

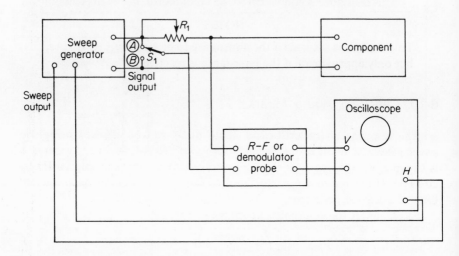

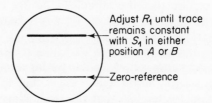

Fig. 8-9. Measuring input impedance.

2. Place the oscilloscope in operation (Chapter 5). Switch off internal recurrent sweep. Set the oscilloscope sweep selector and sync selector to external.

3. Place the sweep generator in operation as described in its instruction manual. Switch sweep generator blanking control on or off as desired. Tune the sweep generator to the normal operating frequency with which the component is to be used. Adjust the sweep width to cover the complete range of frequencies.

4. Set switch S_1 to the A position.

5. Adjust the sweep generator output level so that the trace is set at a convenient vertical scale marking. Note this vertical deflection scale marking.

6. Move the test switch S_1 from position A to position B.

7. Adjust resistor R_1 until the voltage indicated on the oscilloscope is the same in both positions of switch S_1.
8. Disconnect resistor R_1 from the circuit and measure its d-c resistance. This resistance is equivalent to the input impedance of the component.

NOTE

This method is accurate if the impedance to be measured is *resistive*, but only approximate if the impedance is reactive.

8-10. Checking Audio Filters

The response characteristics of audio filters can be checked using the sweep generator/oscilloscope combination, provided that the sweep generator is capable of sweeping over the audio range (from approximately 20 Hz to 20 kHz). If maximum accuracy is desired, an audio oscillator must also be used as a marker generator.

1. Connect the equipment as shown in Fig. 8-10.

NOTE

Resistors R_1 and R_2 are included since many test specifications for filters require that the input and output be terminated in their respective impedances. R_1 and R_2 may be omitted unless required by specification.

2. Place the oscilloscope in operation (Chapter 5). Switch off internal recurrent sweep. Set the oscilloscope sweep selector and sync selector to external.
3. Place the sweep generator in operation as described in its instruction manual. Switch sweep generator blanking control on or off as desired. Adjust the sweep generator to cover the complete audio range, or that portion of the range which would affect filter operation.
4. Check the filter response curve appearing on the oscilloscope against those of Fig. 8-10, or against the filter specifications. Typical high-pass, low-pass, bandpass, and band-suppression response curves are shown in Fig. 8-10.
5. If it is desired to determine the exact frequencies at which filter response occurs, the audio marker generator can be adjusted until the marker pip is aligned at the point of interest. The frequency, or band of frequencies, can be read from the audio marker frequency dial.
6. The amplitude of any point on the response curve can be measured directly on the oscilloscope (assuming that the vertical system is volt-age-calibrated).

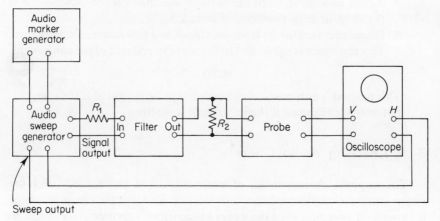

$R_1 =$ filter input impedance
$R_2 =$ filter output impedance

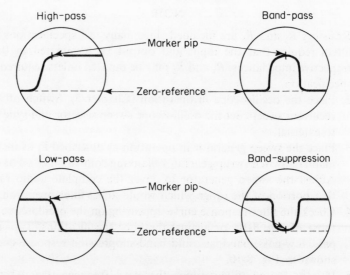

Fig. 8-10. Checking audio filters.

8-11. Sweep Frequency Alignment of Receivers

As stated in Sec. 8-1, the sweep generator/oscilloscope combination can be used most effectively in sweep alignment of receivers. Procedures for sweep generator/oscilloscope alignment of AM and FM communications receivers are given in Chapter 11. Chapter 13 gives procedures for sweep alignment of TV receivers.

CHAPTER 9

Checking
Individual Components

An oscilloscope is particularly useful in checking those components where response curves, transient characteristics, phase relationship, and time are of special importance. Of course, any component that can be checked by a voltmeter can also be checked with an oscilloscope, since the oscilloscope will function as an a-c or d-c voltmeter. If a component requires only a voltage check (or resistance check) it is more economical and practical to use a simple multitester.

This chapter describes the procedures for checking those components where an oscilloscope would provide a better or faster method. In most cases, similar tests could be made without an oscilloscope, but that would involve making a series of many tests, and then plotting the data as a curve or graph. The oscilloscope method presents the information instantly.

9-1. Checking Semiconductor Rectifiers

A d-c oscilloscope can be used to display and measure the current-voltage characteristics of semiconductor rectifiers, but both the vertical and horizontal channels must be voltage-calibrated. The procedures for voltage calibration of the vertical channel are given in Chapter 6. The same procedures can be applied to the horizontal channel, so that a volts/division calibration is obtained instead of the usual time/division. Also, the horizontal and vertical channels must be identical, or nearly identical, to eliminate any phase difference. Section 7-9 describes the procedures for determining the phase difference between the horizontal and vertical channels.

As shown in Fig. 9-1, the semiconductor rectifier is tested by applying

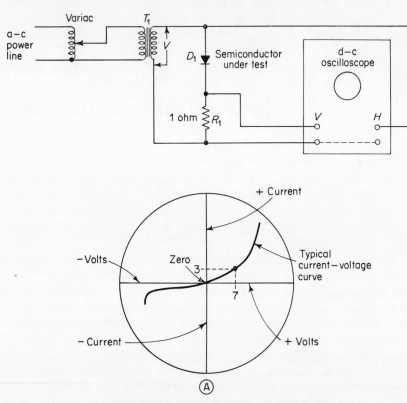

Fig. 9-1. Checking semiconductor rectifiers.

a controlled a-c voltage across the anode and cathode, through resistor R_1. The a-c voltage (set to the maximum rated capacity of the rectifier) alternately biases the anode positive and negative, causing both forward and reverse current to flow through R_1. The voltage drop across R_1 is applied to the vertical channel and causes the spot to move up and down. Therefore, vertical deflection is proportional to current. The vertical scale divisions can be converted directly to current when R_1 is made 1 ohm. For example, a 3-volt vertical deflection indicates a 3-amp current.

The same voltage applied across the semiconductor rectifier is applied to the horizontal channel (which has been voltage calibrated) and causes the spot to move right or left. Therefore, horizontal deflection is proportional to voltage. The combination of the horizontal (voltage) deflection and vertical (current) deflection, causes the spot to trace out the complete current-voltage characteristics.

1. Connect the equipment as shown in Fig. 9-1.
2. Place the oscilloscope in operation (Chapter 5). Voltage-calibrate both the vertical and horizontal channels as necessary (Chapter 6). The spot should be at the vertical and horizontal center with no signal applied to either channel.
3. Switch off the internal recurrent sweep. Set sweep selector and sync selector to external. Leave the horizontal and vertical gain controls set at the (voltage) calibrate position.
4. Adjust the variac so that the voltage applied across the semiconductor rectifier D_1 under test is the maximum rated value.
5. Check the oscilloscope pattern against the typical curves of Fig. 9-1 and/or against the rectifier specifications. Figure 9-1a is a typical response pattern. Compare the current-voltage values against the specified values. For example, assume that a current of 3 amp should flow with 7 volts applied. This can be checked by measuring along the horizontal scale to the 7-volt point, then measuring from that point up or down to the trace. The 7-volt (horizontal) point should intersect the trace at the 3-amp (vertical) point.

9-2. Checking Semiconductor Diodes for Current-voltage Characteristics

Procedures for checking the current-voltage characteristics of a semiconductor diode (small signal diode) are the same as for semiconductor rectifiers (Sec. 9-1). There is one major difference. In a small-signal diode, the ratio of forward voltage to reverse voltage is usually quite large. A forward voltage of the same amplitude as the rated reverse voltage will probably damage the diode. Likewise, if the voltage is lowered for both forward and reverse directions, this will not provide a realistic value in the reverse direction.

Ideally, a small-signal diode should be tested with a low-value forward voltage, and a high-value reverse voltage. This can be accomplished using a circuit as shown in Fig. 9-2. The circuit of Fig. 9-2 is essentially the same as that of Fig. 9-1, except that rectifiers CR_1 and CR_2 are included to conduct on alternate half-cycles of the voltage across transformer T_1 secondary. Rectifiers CR_1 and CR_2 are chosen for a linear amount of conduction near zero.

The variac is adjusted for maximum-rated reverse voltage across the diode D_1, as applied through CR_2 when upper secondary terminal of T_1 goes negative. This applies the full reverse voltage.

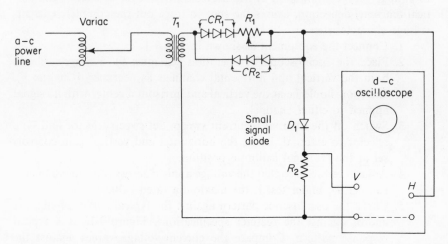

Fig. 9-2. Checking semiconductor (small signal) diodes.

Resistor R_1 is adjusted for maximum-rated forward voltage across the diode D_1, as applied through CR_1 when the upper secondary terminal of T_1 goes positive. This applies a forward voltage, as limited by R_1.

With resistor R_1 properly adjusted, perform the current-voltage check as described in Sec. 9-1.

9-3. Checking Semiconductor Diodes for Switching Time

An oscilloscope having wide frequency response and good transient characteristics can be used to check the high-speed switch and recovery time of diodes used in computers. The oscilloscope vertical channel must be voltage-calibrated in the normal manner; the horizontal channel should be time-calibrated (rather than sweep-frequency-calibrated).

As shown in Fig. 9-3, the semiconductor diode is tested by applying a forward-biased current (I_f, Fig. 9-3a) from the B+ supply, adjusted by R_2 and measured by M_1. A negative square wave is developed across R_3. This square wave switches the diode voltage rapidly to a high negative value. The diode does not cut off immediately. Instead, a steep transient is developed by the high, momentary current flow.The reverse current falls to its low steady-state value when the carriers are removed from the junction. The square wave is thus converted to the shape shown in Fig. 9-3a by the diode.

Both forward and reverse currents are passed through resistor R_3. The voltage drop across R_4 is applied through emitter follower Q_1 to the oscilloscope vertical channel. The coaxial cable provides some delay so that the complete waveform will be displayed.

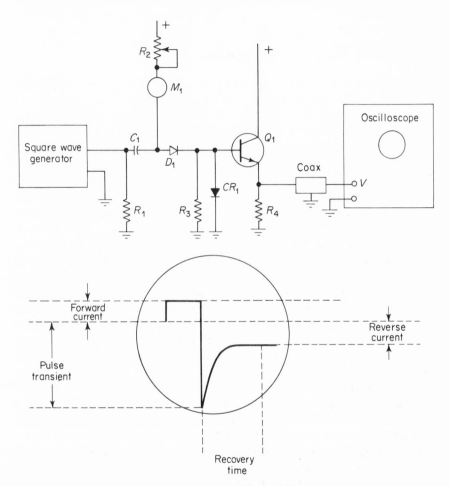

Fig. 9-3. Checking semicondutor diodes for switching time.

1. Connect the equipment as shown in Fig. 9-3.
2. Place the oscilloscope in operation (Chapter 5).
3. Switch on the internal recurrent sweep. Set sweep selector and sync selector to internal.
4. Set the square-wave generator to a repetition rate of 100 kHz, or as specified in the diode manufacturer's data.
5. Set R_1 for the specified forward test current, as measured on M_1.

6. Increase the square-wave generator output level until a pattern appears.
7. If necessary, readjust the sweep and sync controls until a single pulse is shown.
8. Measure the recovery time along the horizontal (time-calibrated) axis.

9-4. Testing Magnetic Components

Hysteresis and saturation are the most important properties of magnetic components that can be checked with an oscilloscope. Both vertical and horizontal channels must, however, be voltage-calibrated. The procedures for voltage calibration of the vertical channel are given in Chapter 6. The same procedures can be applied to the horizontal channel, so that a volt/division calibration is obtained instead of the usual time/division. Also, the horizontal and vertical channels must be identical, or nearly identical, to eliminate any phase difference. Section 7-9 describes the procedures for determining the phase difference between the horizontal and vertical channels.

As shown in Fig. 9-4, the magnetic component under test is connected in series with a noninductive resistance R_1 of approximately 1–10 ohms. If the magnetic component is a material (such as a magnetic core) rather than a complete component, a temporary coil may be wound around the sample material. The material or component is tested by applying a sine wave of sufficient amplitude to produce saturation across both the component and the resistor R_1. The voltage drop across R_1 is applied to the vertical channel, and causes the spot to move up and down. Therefore, vertical deflection is proportional to current through the magnetic device. In turn, this current is proportional to flux density.

The same voltage applied across the magnetic device and R_1 is applied to the horizontal channel (which has been voltage-calibrated to match the vertical channel), and causes the spot to move right or left. Therefore, horizontal deflection is proportional to voltage. In turn, this voltage is proportional to magnetizing force.

The combination of the horizontal (magnetizing force) and vertical (flux density) deflection, causes the spot to trace out the hysteresis-saturation curve. The presence of a double trace indicates hysteresis.

NOTE

Not all the many magnetic-core components used in electronics (computer memory cores, transformers, saturable reactors, choke coils, magnetic amplifiers, etc.) are expected to show hysteresis. In transformers, for example, the effects of hysteresis produce loss and

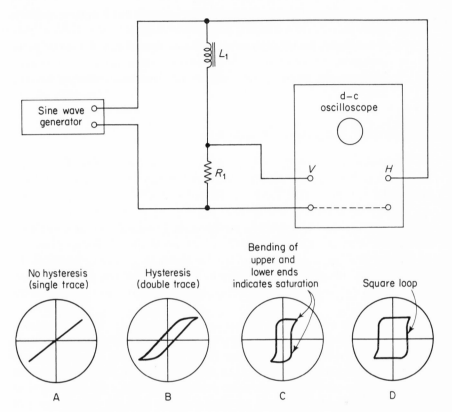

Fig. 9-4. Testing magnetic components for hysteresis and saturation.

are not desired. On the other hand, the material for a magnetic amplifier or computer should show specific hysteresis effects. In either extreme, the presence or absence of hysteresis can be determined at a glance by using an oscilloscope. Then, if desired, the the amount of hysteresis can be measured.

1. Connect the equipment as shown in Fig. 9-4.
2. Place the oscilloscope in operation (Chapter 5). Voltage-calibrate both the vertical and horizontal channels as necessary (Chapter 6). The spot should be at the vertical and horizontal center with no signal applied to either channel.
3. Switch off the internal recurrent sweep. Set sweep selector and sync selector to external. Leave the horizontal and vertical gain controls set at the (voltage) calibrate position.
4. Set the generator to the desired test frequency. Increase the generator output, noting that the pattern enlarges on the screen, both horizontally and vertically. Continue to increase generator output until the

upper and lower ends of the pattern bend as saturation is reached.

5. Using the voltage-calibrated horizontal axis, measure the peak voltage at which saturation occurs.

6. Using the voltage-calibrated vertical axis, measure the peak voltage at which saturation occurs. This voltage can be converted to current (through the device under test), using the value of R_1 in a basic Ohm's law equation. For example, if the vertical deflection voltage is 10 millivolts, and the value of R_1 is 1 ohm, the current through the magnetic component under test is 10 milliamp.

7. Compare the voltage and current values of the hysteresis loop against the manufacturer's specifications. On those devices expected to show hysteresis, the square loop shown in Fig. 9-4d is usually specified as ideal. This is not always the case.

NOTE

In many specifications for magnetic core material, the matter of particular importance is the area of the hysteresis loop, rather than the voltage and current values. The area can be readily measured by using the oscilloscope screen divisions. In other specifications, the flux density (B) or vertical deflection is specified in gausses; the magnetizing force (H) or horizontal deflection is specified in oersteds. Although it is usually not practical to calibrate the scale divisions on oersteds and gausses, the scale divisions above the zero line are related to $+$gausses; the divisions below the zero line are related to $-$gausses; divisions to the right of the vertical center line are related to $+$oersteds, and the divisions to the left of the vertical center line are related to $-$oersteds.

9-5. Testing Ferroelectric Components

Many ferroelectric materials exhibit electrostatic hysteresis and saturation. It is possible to measure the hysteresis and saturation of these ferroelectric materials using an oscilloscope. The procedure is almost identical to that for magnetic components as described in Sec. 9-4. The major differences in the procedure are as follows:

The equipment is connected as shown in Fig. 9-5. A fixed capacitor C_1 is used in place of resistor R_1. Vertical deflection is proportional to the voltage developed across C_1. If the ferroelectric component is a material rather than a complete component, a flat slab of the material can be placed between two metal plates.

Vertical deflection is proportional to electric charge Q (with $+$coulombs above the zero line, and $-$coulombs below). Horizontal deflection is proportional to applied voltage V (+volts to the right of the vertical center line, and −volts to the left of the vertical center line).

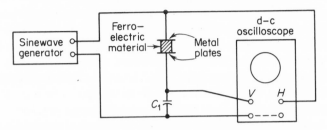

Fig. 9-5. Testing ferroelectric components for hysteresis and saturation.

9-6. Testing Transistors for Collector Current versus Emitter Current

A d-c oscilloscope can be used to display and measure the collector-current–emitter-current characteristics of transistors. Both the vertical and horizontal channels must be voltage-calibrated. The procedures for voltage calibration of the vertical channel are given in Chapter 6. The same procedures can be applied to the horizontal channel, so that a volts/division calibration is obtained instead of the usual time/division. The horizontal zero reference point should, however, be at the left (or right) of the screen rather than in the center. Also, the horizontal and vertical channels must be identical, or nearly identical, in order to eliminate any phase difference. Section 7-9 describes the procedures for determining the phase difference between the horizontal and vertical channels.

As shown in Fig. 9-6, the transistor is tested by applying a controlled d-c voltage to the collector. The collector voltage is developed by rectifying the transformer T_1 secondary voltage with diode CR_1. Collector voltage can be adjusted to any desired value by the variac. When collector current flows on positive half-cycles, the current flows through resistor R_1. The voltage drop across R_1 is applied to the vertical channel and causes the spot to move up and down. Therefore, vertical deflection is proportional to current. The vertical scale divisions can be converted directly to current when R_1 is made 1 ohm. With R_1 at a value of 10 ohms, the indicated voltage value must be divided by 10 to obtain current. For example, a 3-volt vertical deflection indicates a 0.3 amp current.

The same voltage applied to the transistor collector is applied to the horizontal channel (which has been voltage-calibrated), and causes the spot to move from left to right (for the *n-p-n* transistor shown). Therefore, horizontal deflection is proportional to voltage. The combination of the horizontal (voltage) deflection and vertical (current) deflection causes the spot to trace out the collector-current–collector-voltage characteristic of the transistor.

Usually, the change in collector current for a given change in emitter current is the desired characteristic for most transistors. This can be displayed by setting the emitter current to a given value and measuring the collector-current curve, with a given collector voltage. Then the emitter current is changed to another value, and the new collector current is displayed, without changing the collector voltage. Collector voltage is set by the variac. Emitter current is set by R_2 and measured on M_1.

The test connection diagram of Fig. 9-6 is for an *n-p-n* transistor connected in a common-emitter circuit. If a *p-n-p* transistor is to be tested, the polarity of rectifier CR_1, battery B, and meter M_1 must be reversed. Also, horizontal zero reference point should be at the right of the screen rather than at the left.

The following procedure will display a single curve. There are commercial

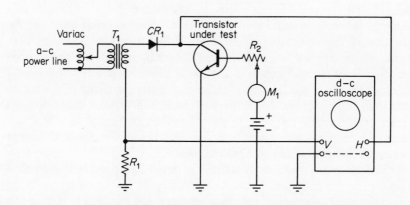

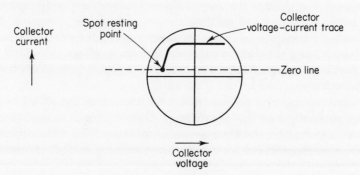

Fig. 9-6. Testing transistors for collector current versus emitter current.

transistor test units that will trace several curves (one for each value of emitter current). Such test units are usually found as complete special-purpose oscilloscopes (such as the Tektronix Type 575).

1. Connect the equipment as shown in Fig. 9-6.
2. Place the oscilloscope in operation (Chapter 5). Voltage-calibrate both the vertical and horizontal channels as necessary (Chapter 6). The spot should be at the vertical center, and at the left (for *n-p-n*) of the horizontal center with no signal applied to either channel.
3. Switch off the internal recurrent sweep. Set sweep selector and sync selector to external. Leave the horizontal and vertical gain controls set at the (voltage) calibrate position. Set the vertical polarity switch so that the trace will deflect up from the center line as shown in Fig. 9-6a.
4. Adjust the variac so that the voltage applied to the collector is the maximum rated value. This voltage can be read on the voltage-calibrated horizontal scale.
5. Adjust resistor R_2 for the desired emitter current as indicated on meter M_1.
6. Check the oscilloscope pattern against the transistor specifications. Compare the current-voltage values against the specified values. For example, assume that a collector current of 300 milliamp should flow with 7 volts applied. This can be checked by measuring along the horizontal scale to the 7-volt point, then measuring from that point up to the trace. The 7-volt (horizontal) point should intersect the trace at the 300-milliamp (3 volt) vertical point.
7. If desired, adjust resistor R_2 for another emitter current value as indicated on meter M_1. Then check the new collector current–voltage curve.

9-7. Testing Transistors for Switching Time

An oscilloscope having wide frequency response, good transient charac-teristics, and a dual trace can be used to check the high-speed switching characteristics of transistors used in computers. The oscilloscope vertical channel must be voltage-calibrated in the normal manner; the horizontal channel should be time-calibrated (rather than sweep-frequency calibrated).

As shown in Fig. 9-7, the transistor is tested by applying a pulse to the base of the transistor under test. This same pulse is applied to one of the oscilloscope vertical inputs. The transistor collector output is applied to the other oscilloscope vertical input (inverted 180° by the common-emitter circuit). The two pulses are then compared as to rise time, fall time, delay time, and storage time. The transistor output pulse characteristics can then be compared with the transistor specifications.

1. Connect the equipment as shown in Fig. 9-7.

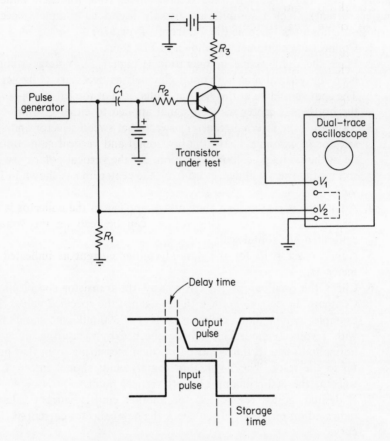

Fig. 9-7. Testing transistor switching time.

2. Place the oscilloscope in operation (Chapter 5). Switch on the internal recurrent sweep; set sweep selector and sync selector to internal.

3. Set the pulse generator to produce a 3-volt, 5-microsecond positive pulse. These values are arbitrary, but are typical for computer transistors. Always use the values specified in the transistor manufacurer's data.

4. Adjust the collector and base supply voltages to the values specified in the transistor manufactuer's data.

5. The oscilloscope pattern should appear as shown in Fig. 9-7b, with both the transistor output pulse and imput pulse displayed.

6. Measure the rise time, fall time and delay time along the horizontal (time-calibrated) axis as shown in Fig. 12-1. Storage time measurement is shown in Fig. 9-7.

9-8. Checking Tunnel Diode
Negative Resistance Characteristics

A d-c oscilloscope can be used to display and measure the negative-resistance characteristics of tunnel diodes. Both the vertical and horizontal channels must be voltage calibrated. The procedures for voltage calibration of the vertical channel are given in Chapter 6. The same procedures can be applied to the horizontal channel so that a volts/division calibration is obtained instead of the usual time/division. The horizontal and vertical zero reference point should, however, be at the lower left of the screen rather than in the center. Also, the horizontal and vertical channels must be identical, or nearly identical, in order to eliminate any phase difference. Section 7-9 describes the procedures for determining the phase difference between the horizontal and vertical channels.

As shown in Fig. 9-8, the tunnel diode is tested by applying a controlled d-c voltage across the diode, through resistor R_3. This d-c voltage is developed by rectifier CR_1, and is controlled by the variac. Current through the tunnel diode also flows through R_3. The voltage drop across R_3 is applied to the vertical channel and causes the spot to move up and down. Therefore, vertical deflection is proportional to current. The vertical scale division can be converted directly to current when R_1 is made 1 ohm. The indicated voltage value must be divided by 10 to obtain current. For example, a 3-volt vertical deflection indicates 0.3 amp.

The same voltage applied across the tunnel diode is applied to the horizontal channel (which has been voltage-calibrated), and causes the spot to move from left to right. Therefore, horizontal deflection is proportional to voltage. The combination of the horizontal (voltage) deflections and vertical (current) deflection causes the spot to trace out the complete negative-resistance characteristics.

1. Connect the equipment as shown in Fig. 9-8.
2. Place the oscilloscope in operation (Chapter 5). Voltage calibrate both the vertical and horizontal channels as necessary (Chapter 6). The spot should be at the lower left-hand side of center with no signal applied to either channel.
3. Switch off the internal recurrent sweep. Set sweep selector and sync selector to external. Leave the horizontal and vertical gain controls set at the (voltage) calibrate position.
4. Adjust the variac so that the voltage applied across the tunnel diode under test is the maximum rated forward voltage. This can be read across the voltage-calibrated horizontal axis.
5. Check the oscilloscope pattern against the typical curve of Fig. 9-8a, or against the tunnel diode manufacturer's data.

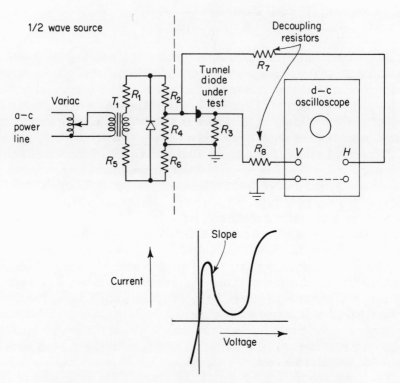

Fig. 9-8. Checking tunnel diode negative resistance characteristics.

9-9. Using an Oscilloscope as the Null Detector of an A-C Bridge

It is possible to use an oscilloscope, instead of a voltmeter, as the null detector of an a-c bridge. An oscilloscope offers the advantage of indicating both reactive balance and resistive balance.

As shown in Fig. 9-9, the source voltage is applied to the bridge input and to the oscilloscope horizontal channel through a phase-shift network. The bridge output is applied to the oscilloscope vertical channel.

1. Connect the equipment as shown in Fig. 9-9.
2. Place the oscilloscope in operation (Chapter 5). Switch off the internal recurrent sweep. Set sweep selector and sync selector to external.
3. Connect the unknown test component (inductor, capacitor, resistor, etc.) to the appropriate bridge terminals.
4. Leave the bridge unbalanced. Adjust R_1 until the oscilloscope pattern becomes an ellipse. If necessary, adjust the horizontal and vertical gain controls to produce an ellipse of suitable size on the oscilloscope screen.

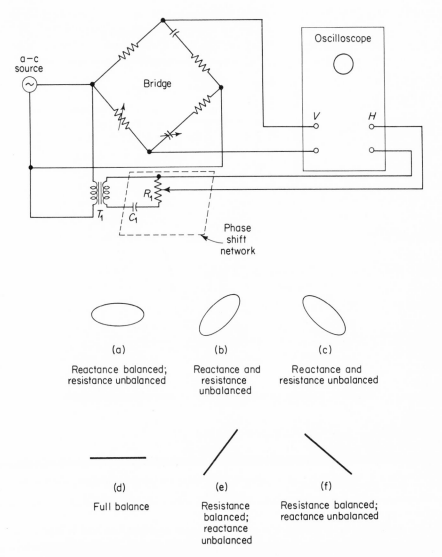

Fig. 9-9. Using an oscilloscope as the null dectector of an a-c bridge.

5. Note the position of the ellipse. When the reactance is balanced (reactance null), the ellipse will be horizontal, as shown in Fig. 9-9a. If the ellipse is slanted to right or left, as shown in Fig. 9-9b or c, the reactance is unbalanced. Adjust the bridge reactance control until the ellipse is horizontal (Fig. 9-9a). Read the reactance of the unknown component from the bridge reactance control.

6. Adjust the bridge resistance control until the ellipse is closed into a straight line.

7. When both the reactance and resistance are balanced, a straight horizontal line is obtained, as shown in Fig. 9-9d. If only the resistance is balanced, the trace will be a straight line, but the line will be tilted to left or right, as shown in Fig. 9-9e or f.

9-10. Checking Potentiometers

An oscilloscope can be used to check the noise (both static and dynamic) of a potentiometer, rheostat, variable resistor, or slider resistance. Static potentiometer "noise" is a result of any current variation due to poor contact, when the contact arm is at rest. Dynamic noise is the amount of irregular current variation, when the contact arm is in motion.

As shown in Fig. 9-10, a constant direct current is applied through the

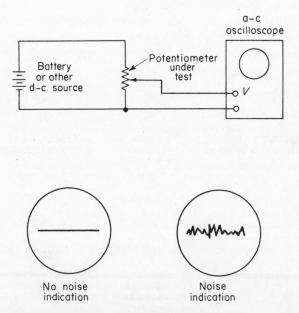

Fig. 9-10. Checking potentiometers for dynamic and static noise.

potentiometer by means of an external source. A battery is the best source, since it is free of any noise or ripple. An output voltage from the potentiometer is applied to the oscilloscope vertical channel. The internal recurrent sweep can be used, provided that the sweep frequency is above about 100 Hz. If the potentiometer is "quiet," there will be a straight horizontal trace, with no vertical deflection. Any vertical deflection indicates noise.

1. Connect the equipment as shown in Fig. 9-10.
2. Place the oscilloscope in operation (Chapter 5). Switch on the internal

recurrent sweep. Set the sync selector to external so that the sweep will not be triggered by noise, if any.

NOTE

An a-c oscilloscope is recommended for this test since the voltage divider action of the potentiometer would move the trace vertically on a d-c oscilloscope.

3. Measure the static noise level, if any, on the voltage-calibrated vertical scale. It is possible that a noise indication could be caused by pickup in the lead wires. If in doubt, disconnect the leads from the potentiometer, but not from the oscilloscope. If the noise is still present, it is pick-up noise. If the noise is removed, it is static noise (probably due to poor contact of the potentiometer arm).

4. Vary the potentiometer contact arm from one extreme to the other. Measure the dynamic noise level, if any, on the voltage-calibrated scale. Dynamic noise should not be difficult to distinguish since it occurs only when the contact arm is in motion. (On commercial test units, the contact arm is driven by a motor.)

NOTE

The dynamic noise level will usually be increased if the battery voltage (or other source) is increased. Do not exceed the maximum rated voltage of the potentiometer when making these tests.

9-11. Checking Relays

An oscilloscope can be used to check the make and break of relay contacts. The presence of contact "bounce," as well as the actual make-time and break-time of the contacts can be displayed and measured. To be effective, the oscilloscope should be capable of single sweep operation (Chapter 2). Also, because of the instantaneous nature of the trace, the display should be photographed (unless a storage-type oscilloscope is used).

NOTE

A storage oscilloscope is often used to display instantaneous "one shot" traces. The storage oscilloscope will hold a display for an indefinite period until it is removed by operating an "erase" control. Because the storage oscilloscope is a special-purpose instrument, it is not covered in this book. The techniques for operating a storage oscilloscope and for photographing the stored display are covered thoroughly in the instruction manuals for the instruments.

Figure 9-11a is the connection diagram for testing a d-c relay. When

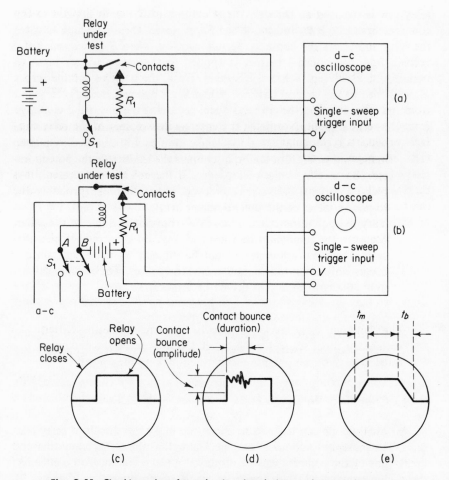

Fig. 9-11. Checking relays for make-time, break-time, and contact bounce.

S_1 is closed, a d-c voltage from the external battery is applied to the sweep trigger input to initiate a single sweep. Current is also applied through the relay under test, and causes the relay contacts to close. When the contacts close, the positive voltage across R_1 is applied to the vertical channel. When S_1 is opened, the d-c voltage is removed and the relay contacts open, removing the positive voltage from the vertical input. Normally, the opening and closing of the relay contacts produces a rectangular trace similar to that of Fig. 9-11c. If the contacts are bouncing, the display will be similar to that of Fig. 9-11d. The make-time and break-time of the relay can be measured on the time-calibrated horizontal axis (Fig. 9-11e). The value of R_1 is chosen to limit the relay contact current to the value specified by the manufacturer's data.

Figure 9-11b is the connection diagram for testing an a-c relay. The relay coil is supplied ac through the A contact of S_1; dc is applied to the contacts through the B contacts. When S_{1A} is closed, the a-c voltage actuates the relay and closes the contacts. Simultaneously, when S_{1B} is closed, a d-c voltage from the external battery is applied to the sweep trigger input to initiate a single sweep. When the contacts close, the positive voltage across R_1 is applied to the vertical channel. When S_{1A} is opened, the ac is removed from the relay coil, and the contacts open, removing the positive d-c voltage from the vertical input. Normally, the opening and closing of the relay contacts produce a rectangular trace similar to that of Fig. 9-11c. If the contacts are bouncing, the display will be similar to that of Fig. 9-11d. A-c relays may also exhibit contact "chatter." This shows up as a ripple along the normally flat top of the trace. The make-time and break-time of the relay can be measured along the time calibrated horizontal axis. Again, the value of R_1 is chosen so that the relay contact current limit will not be exceeded.

1. Connect the equipment as shown in Fig. 9-11a or 9-11b, as applicable.
2. Place the oscilloscope in operation (Chapter 5). Set the oscilloscope to single sweep mode. Set the sync selector to external, or as necessary so that the oscilloscope will be triggered by the external d-c voltage. Set up the oscilloscope camera as necessary.
3. If the trace is to be photographed, hold the camera shutter open, close and open switch S_1, then close the camera shutter and develop the picture.
4. Using the developed photo, measure the bounce (if any) amplitude along the vertical axis, and the bounce duration along the horizontal axis (Fig. 9-11d).
5. Measure the make-time, t_m (interval between application of voltage and actual closure of contacts), and break-time, t_b (interval between interruption of voltage and opening of the relay contacts) along the horizontal axis (Fig. 9-11e).

9-12. Checking Vibrators

An oscilloscope can be used to check the make and break of vibrator contacts, as well as to display the operation of synchronous and nonsynchronous vibrator power supplies under actual operating condition. Vibrators are best tested by observing contact operation with the vibrator in the power supply. The approximate square wave across the power supply transformer primary is displayed on the oscilloscope, and is compared against an "ideal" waveform.

Figure 9-12a is the connection diagram for testing synchronous and nonsynchronous vibrators. Figure 9-12b is an "ideal" waveform for a typical vibrator power supply.

1. Connect the equipment as shown in Fig. 9-12a.

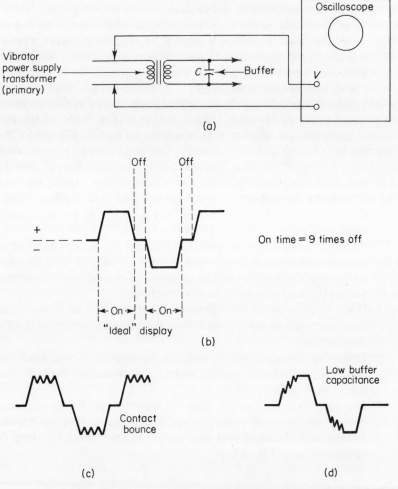

Fig. 9-12. Checking synchronous and nonsynchronous vibrators and vibrator power supplies.

2. Place the oscilloscope in operation (Chapter 5). Switch on the internal recurrent sweep. Set the sync selector and sweep selector to internal. Adjust the sweep frequency and sync controls for one (or preferably, two) stationary cycles on the oscilloscope screen.

3. Compare the actual oscilloscope display with the "ideal" display of Fig. 9-12b. Measure the display amplitude along the vertical axis. Measure the on-time and off-time of the display along the horizontal axis.

4. Usually, the display amplitudes + and − should be equal, although the actual amplitude is not critical.
5. In most vibrator power supplies, the on-time total should be approximately 9 times the off-time total. (The on-time intervals represent the length of time the vibrator contacts are actually closed, and delivering current. The off-time intervals represent the length of time the vibrator contacts are open.)
6. In addition to showing the power supply efficiency (on-time to off-time percentage), the waveform display can also show such conditions as contact bounce (Fig. 9-12c), or insufficient buffer capacitance (Fig. 9-12d).

9-13. Checking Choppers

An oscilloscope can be used to check the operation of electromechanical and electronic choppers. Such choppers are similar in function to vibrators, in that they convert direct current into alternating current for further amplification. (A typical example of chopper use is to convert d-c signals into ac for application to an a-c amplifier within an oscilloscope or electronic voltmeter.) Electromechanical choppers differ from vibrators in that they are driven by an external alternating current source, independent of the direct current source to be converted. The resultant output is a square wave that is proportional to the d-c input. Electronic choppers are essentially electronic switches that produce a square-wave output, proportional to d-c input.

Figure 9-13a is the connection diagram for testing an electromechanical chopper.

Figure 9-13b is the connection diagram for testing an electronic chopper.

1. Connect the equipment as shown in Fig. 9-13a or 9-13b, as applicable.
2. Place the oscilloscope in operation (Chapter 5). Switch on the internal recurrent sweep. Set the sync selector and sweep selector to internal. Adjust the sweep frequency and sync controls for one (or, preferably, two) stationary cycles on the oscilloscope screen.
3. Measure the display amplitude along the vertical axis. Measure the on-time and off-time of the display along the horizontal axis.

NOTE

The square wave characteristics for choppers are similar to those of vibrators (Fig. 9-12).

4. It is also possible to check the chopper output for electrical noise. All test connections remain the same, except that the d-c input voltage

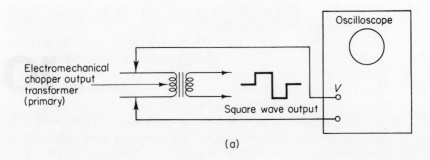

(a)

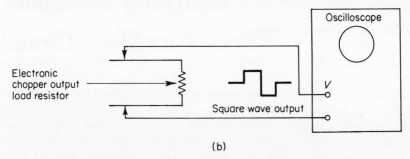

(b)

Fig. 9-13. Checking electromechanical and electronic choppers.

is removed. Under these conditions, any vertical deflection is the result of electrical noise.

NOTE

An electronic chopper should be tested for noise with the d-c input terminals open. An electromechanical chopper should be tested both ways, first with the d-c input terminals shorted, then open.

CHAPTER 10

Checking Amplifiers
and Amplifier Circuits

An oscilloscope is the most logical instrument for checking amplifiers, whether they are complete audio amplifier systems or the audio circuits of a receiver. The oscilloscope will duplicate every function of an electronic voltmeter in troubleshooting, signal tracing, and performance-testing audio equipment. In addition, the oscilloscope offers the advantage of a visual display for such common audio equipment conditions as distortion, hum, noise, ripple, and oscillation.

This chapter describes the basic procedures for using an oscilloscope to test and troubleshoot audio equipment. A competent technician can expand these procedures to perform a very large number of functions when it is realized that the oscilloscope is basically an electronic voltmeter and/or signal tracer that provides a simultaneous display of audio waveforms.

Although it is possible to use almost any oscilloscope effectively in audio work, it is recommended that the vertical amplifier have a good frequency response up to about 500 kHz. This will insure that any harmonics or overtones will be properly amplified and displayed, even though the audio range extends to only about 20 kHz, and manufacturers of the most advanced high-fidelity equipment claim bandpass characteristics no higher than 100 kHz.

10-1. Audio Signal Tracing with an Oscilloscope

An oscilloscope is used in a manner similar to that of an electronic voltmeter when signal tracing audio circuits. A sine wave (or square wave) is introduced into the input by means of an external generator. The amplitude and waveform of the input signal are measured on the oscilloscope. In this application, the voltage is measured on the vertical scale as described in Chapter 6. The oscilloscope probe is then moved to the input and output of each stage, in turn, until the final output (usually at a loudspeaker or output transformer) is reached. The gain of each stage is measured as a voltage on the oscilloscope vertical scale. In addition, it is possible to observe any change in waveform from that applied to the input by the external generator. Thus, stage gain and distortion (if any) are established quickly with an oscilloscope.

1. Connect the equipment as shown in Fig. 10-1.
2. Place the oscilloscope in operation (Chapter 5). Switch on the internal recurrent sweep. Set the sweep selector and sync selector to internal.

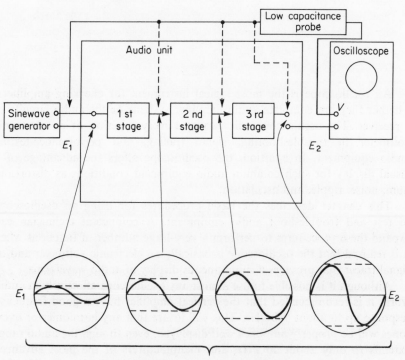

Amplitude increases with each stage
waveform remains substantially the same

Fig. 10-1. Basic audio signal tracing with an oscilloscope.

3. Place the generator in operation as described in its instruction manual. Unless otherwise specified by amplifier data, set the generator output frequency to 1000 Hz. Set the generator output level to the value recommended in the amplifier manufacturer's data. Do not overload the amplifier.

4. With the oscilloscope probe (low-capacitance) connected to the generator output (amplifier input), adjust the sweep frequency controls to diaplay one or two complete cycles on the screen.

5. Move the oscilloscope probe to the output of the first amplifier stage. Measure the voltage gain as described in Chapter 6. Compare the waveform at the stage output with that of the stage input. Normally, the waveform should be substantially the same, except for amplitude.

6. Repeat Step 5 for each stage of the amplifier, from input to output. If the waveform at a stage output is absent, does not show sufficient gain, or is distorted in any way, it is likely that the particular stage is defective. Usually, voltage/resistance checks or component replacement, will reveal the fault.

NOTE

One factor often overlooked in testing amplifiers is setting the amplifier amplitude and tone controls to their normal operating point, or to some particular point specified in the manufacturer's test data.

7. If it is desired to convert the voltage gain of one stage, a group of stages, or the complete amplifier into decibels, use the equation:

$$\text{db gain} = 20 \log \frac{E_2}{E_1}$$

where E_2 = output voltage (of the stage, stages, or complete amplifier)

E_1 = input voltage

NOTE

Voltage gain is normally measured with a sine-wave input, rather than a square wave or pulse.

8. The gain (or loss) of an audio component, such as a transformer or audio filter, can also be measured as described in Steps 5–7.

10-2. Checking Audio Frequency Response with an Oscilloscope

An oscilloscope can be used to obtain a frequency response curve of an audio amplifier or circuit. In this application, the oscilloscope is used as an audio-frequency voltmeter. The basic method is monitoring the amplifier output with the oscilloscope while applying a constant-amplitude audio signal. The audio signal is varied in frequency (but not amplitude) across the entire audio range. Usually, this is from about 20 Hz to 20 kHz, although some manufacturers specify a response up to 100 kHz. The voltage output at various frequencies across the range is plotted on a graph similar to that shown in Fig. 10-2.

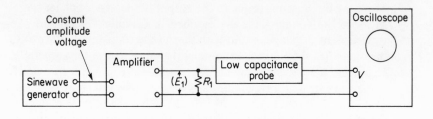

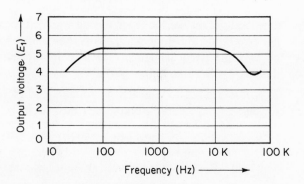

Fig. 10-2. Checking audio frequency response with an oscilloscope.

1. Connect the equipment as shown in Fig. 10-2.
2. Place the oscilloscope in operation (Chapter 5). Switch on the internal recurrent sweep. Set the sweep selector and sync selector to internal.
3. Place the generator in operation as described in its instruction manual. Set the generator output frequency to the lowest point specified in the manufacturer's data. Use a low frequency of approximately 20 Hz in the absence of a specified low limit.
4. With the oscilloscope probe (low-capacitance) connected to the generator output (amplifier input), adjust the sweep frequency controls to display a few cycles on the screen.
5. Set the generator output level to the value recommended in the amplifier manufacturer's data. If no data are available, set the generator

output to an arbitrary value. A simple method of determining a satisfactory input level is to monitor the amplifier output with the oscilloscope and increase the generator output until the waveform just starts to flatten, indicating that the amplifier is being overdriven. Then reduce the generator output until the waveform shows no distortion or flattening. When this point is reached, return the oscilloscope probe to the generator output (amplifier input) and measure the voltage. Keep the generator at this voltage throughout the test.

NOTE

Set the amplifier amplitude and tone controls to their normal operating point, or at the particular setting specified in the manufacturer's test data.

6. Record the amplifier output voltage indication on the graph.
7. Without changing the generator output amplitude, increase the generator frequency by 100 Hz, or as specified in the manufacturer's data. Record the new amplifier output voltage indication on the graph. Repeat this process, checking and recording the amplifier output voltage indication at each frequency point throughout the entire audio range. Draw a line on graph paper through each of the check points in order to obtain a frequency response curve. Usually the curve will resemble that of Fig. 10-2, with a flat portion across the center and a roll-off at each end. Some amplifiers and amplifier circuits are designed to provide a high-frequency boost (where the high end of curve increases in amplitude) or low-frequency boost (where the low end shows an amplitude increase). The manufacturer's data must be consulted for this information.

NOTE

Generator output may vary with changes in frequency, a fact often overlooked in making a frequency response test of an amplifier. Even precision laboratory generators can vary in output with changes in frequency. This could result in considerable error. Therefore it is recommended that the generator output be monitored with the oscilloscope after every change in frequency. Then, if necessary, the generator output amplitude can be reset to the correct value established in Step 5. Within extremes, it is more important that the generator output amplitude remain *constant* rather than at some specific value, when making a frequency response check.

8. Repeat the frequency response check with the tone control set at each of their positions, or as specified in the manufacturer's data.

NOTE

The load resistor R_1 of Fig. 10-2 is used for power amplifiers. Usually manufacturers recommend that power amplifiers not be operated without a load. Also, the load serves to stabilize the amplifier output during test. The value of the load resistor should equal the normal output impedance of the amplifier. If practical, the response curve can be run with the amplifier connected to its normal output load (loudspeakers, etc.), thus eliminating the need for a load resistor.

10-3. Measuring Power Output of an Amplifier

An oscilloscope can be used as an audio-frequency voltmeter to measure the power output of an amplifier or amplifier circuit. The test connections are identical with that of Fig. 10-2.

1. Connect the equipment as shown in Fig. 10-2.
2. Place the oscilloscope in operation (Chapter 5). Switch on the internal recurrent sweep. Set the sweep selector and sync selector to internal.
3. Place the generator in operation as described in its instruction manual. Set the generator output frequency to the point specified in the manufacturer's data. Use a frequency of 1000 Hz in the absence of a specified value.
4. Set the amplifier gain control to maximum and the tone controls to their normal position, unless otherwise specified in the manufacturer's data.

NOTE

The load resistor R_1 (Fig. 10-2) is used for power amplifiers. Usually manufacturers recommend that power amplifiers not be operated without a load. Also, the load serves to stabilize the amplifier output during test. The value of the load resistor should equal the normal output impedance of the amplifier. If practical, the power measurement can be made with the amplifier connected to its normal output load (loudspeakers, etc.), thus eliminating the need for a load resistor.

5. With the oscilloscope probe (low-capacitance) connected to the amplifier output, adjust the sweep frequency controls to display a few cycles on the screen.
6. Set the generator output level to the value recommended in the amplifier manufacturer's data. If no data are available, increase the generator output until the waveform just starts to flatten, indicating that the amplifier is being overdriven. Then reduce the generator output until the waveform shows no distortion or flattening.

7. Measure the maximum output voltage and calculate the power output using the following equation:

$$P = \frac{E^2}{R}$$

where P = power output

E = maximum voltage indicated on oscilloscope

R = value of load resistor R_1

NOTE

Usually, the power output of an amplifier is based on the RMS voltage across a given load, whereas most oscilloscope voltage measurements are peak-to-peak. Refer to Chapter 6 (Fig. 6-2) for the procedure to convert peak-to-peak voltage to RMS voltage.

10-4. Measuring Amplifier Noise and Hum with an Oscilloscope

If the vertical channel of an oscilloscope is sufficiently sensitive, the oscilloscope can be used to check and measure the background noise level of an amplifier, as well as to check for the presence of hum, oscillation, etc. The oscilloscope vertical channel should be capable of a measurable deflection with 1 millivolt or less, since this is the background noise level of some amplifiers. The basic procedure consists of measuring amplifier output with the gain control at maximum, but without an input signal. The oscilloscope is superior to a voltmeter for noise level measurement since the frequency and nature of the noise (or other signal) will be displayed visually.

1. Connect the equipment as shown in Fig. 10-3. The load resistor R_1 is used for power amplifiers and should have a value equal to the amplifier's output impedance.
2. Place the oscilloscope in operation (Chapter 5). Switch on the internal recurrent sweep. Set the sweep selector and sync selector to internal.
3. Set the amplifier gain control to maximum and the tone controls to their normal position, unless otherwise specified in the manufacturer's data.
4. Increase the oscilloscope vertical gain control until there is a noise or "hash" indication.

NOTE

It is possible that a noise indication could be caused by pickup in the lead wires. If in doubt, disconnect the leads from the amplifier, but not from the oscilloscope. If the noise is still present, it is pick-up noise. If the noise is removed, it is amplifier background noise.

5. Measure the noise voltage. This is the total noise voltage, including hum, background noise, oscillation, etc.

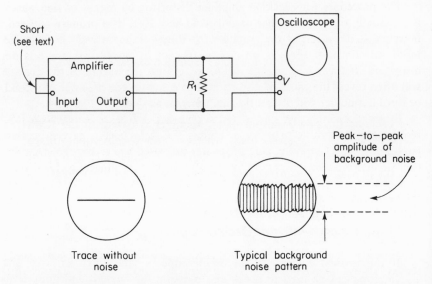

Fig. 10-3. Measuring amplifier noise and hum with an oscilloscope.

6. If it is suspected that there is line hum present in the amplifier output, set the oscilloscope sync control to line. If a stationary signal pattern appears, this is owing to line hum. Measure the amplitude of the line hum, if desired.

7. If a signal appears that is not at the line frequency this can be due to oscillation or stray pickup. Short the amplifier input terminals. If the signal remains, it is probably oscillation. In either case, the oscilloscope can be used to measure both the voltage and frequency of the unknown signal (Chapters 6 and 7).

10-5. Checking Amplifier Distortion

The major advantage of an oscilloscope over a voltmeter in testing amplifiers is the oscilloscope's ability to display distortion. There are many techniques for checking and measuring distortion in audio equipment. A comprehensive discussion of all methods is beyond the scope of this book, as is a description of all causes and cures for distortion. There are four basic methods that involve the use of an oscilloscope: analysis of sine-wave patterns, analysis of square-wave patterns, measurement of harmonic distortion (fundamental suppression method), and measurement of intermodulation distortion.

10-5-1. Checking Distortion by Sine-wave Analysis

The procedure for checking amplifier distortion by means of sine waves is essentially the same as that described in Sec. 10-1. The primary concern, however, is deviation of the amplifier (or stage) output waveform from the input waveform. If there is no change (except in amplitude), there is no distortion. If there is a change in the waveform, the nature of the change will often reveal the cause of distortion. For example, the presence of second or third harmonics will distort the fundamental as shown in Fig. 10-4.

In practice, analyzing sine waves to pinpoint distortion is a difficult job, requiring considerable experience. Unless the distortion is severe, it may pass unnoticed. Therefore, sine waves are best used where harmonic distortion or intermodulation meters are combined with oscilloscopes for distortion analysis. If an oscilloscope is to be used alone, square waves provide the best basis for distortion analysis.

10-5-2. Harmonic Distortion Analysis

No matter what amplifier circuit is used, or how well the circuit is designed, there is always the possibility of odd or even harmonics being present with the fundamental. These harmonics combine with the fundamental and produce distortion, as is the case when any two signals are combined.

Commercial harmonic distortion meters operate on the *fundamental suppression* principle. As shown in Fig. 10-4, a sine wave is applied to the amplifier input, and the output is measured on the oscilloscope. The output is then applied through a filter that suppresses the fundamental frequency. Any output from the filter is then the result of harmonics. This output is also displayed on the oscilloscope where the signal can be checked for frequency to determine the harmonic content. For example, if the input was 1000 Hz, and the output after filtering was 3000 Hz, this would be a result of third harmonic distortion.

The percentage of harmonic distortion can also be determined by this method. For example, if the output without filter was 100 millivolts, and with filter was 3 millivolts, this would indicate a 3 per cent harmonic distortion.

1. Connect the equipment as shown in Fig. 10-4.

NOTE

In some commercial harmonic distortion meters, the filter is tunable so that the amplifier can be tested over a wide range of fundamental frequencies. In other harmonic distortion meters, the filter is fixed frequency, but can be detuned slightly to produce a sharp null.

2. Place the oscilloscope in operation (Chapter 5). Switch on the internal

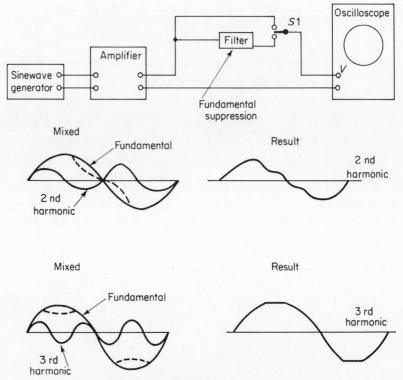

Fig. 10-4. Harmonic distortion analysis.

recurrent sweep. Set the sweep selector and sync selector to internal.

3. Set the amplifier amplitude and tone controls to their normal operating point, or at the particular setting specified in the manufacturer's test data.

4. Place the generator in operation as described in its instruction manual. Set the generator output frequency to the filter null frequency. Set the generator output amplitude to the value recommended in the amplifier manufacturer's data. If no data are available, set switch S_1 to position 1, and increase the generator output until the waveform just starts to flatten indicating that the amplifier is being overdriven. Then reduce the generator output until the waveform shows no distortion or flattening.

5. If necessary, adjust the sweep frequency controls to display a few cycles on the screen.

6. Measure the voltage with switch S_1 in position 1. Record this value as E_1.

7. Set switch S_1 to position 2. Adjust the filter for the deepest null indication on the oscilloscope. Record this value as E_2.

8. Calculate the total harmonic distortion using the equation:

$$D = 100 \frac{E_2}{E_1}$$

where D = percentage of total harmonic distortion

E_1 = output before filtering

E_2 = output after filtering

9. If the filter is tunable, select another frequency, tune the generator to that frequency and repeat the procedure (Steps 4–8).

10-5-3. Intermodulation Distortion Analysis

When two signals of different frequency are mixed in an amplifier, there is a possibility of the lower-frequency signal amplitude modulating the higher-frequency signal. This produces a form of distortion, known as *intermodulation distortion.*

Commercial intermodulation distortion meters consist of a signal generator and high-pass filter as shown in Fig. 10-5. The signal generator portion of the meter produces a high-frequency signal (usually about 7000

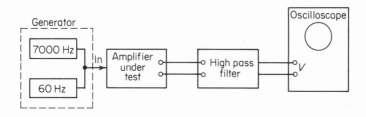

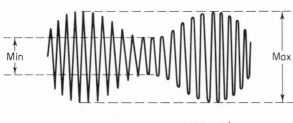

Intermodulation (%) = 100 x $\frac{max-min}{max+min}$

Fig. 10-5. Intermodulation distortion analysis.

Hz) which is modulated by a low-frequency signal (usually 60 Hz). The mixed signals are applied to the amplifier input. The amplifier output is connected through a high-pass filter to the oscilloscope vertical channel. The high-pass filter removes the low-frequency (60 Hz) signal. Therefore, the only signal appearing on the oscilloscope vertical channel should be the high-frequency (7000 Hz). If any 60 Hz is present on the display, it is being passed through as modulation on the 7000 Hz signal.

1. Connect the equipment as shown in Fig. 10-5.
2. Place the oscilloscope in operation (Chapter 5). Switch on the internal recurrent sweep. Set the sweep selector and sync selector to internal.
3. Set the amplifier amplitude and tone controls to their normal operating point, or at the particular setting specified in the manufacturer's test data.
4. Place the generator in operation as described in its instruction manual.
5. If necessary, adjust the sweep frequency controls to display a few cycles on the screen.
6. Measure the vertical dimensions MAX and MIN (Fig. 10-5) in screen divisions.
7. Calculate the total intermodulation distortion using the equation:

$$IM(\%) = 100 \left[\frac{MAX - MIN}{MAX + MIN} \right]$$

where IM $(\%)$ = percentage of total intermodulation
   MIN = modulation minimum dimension
   MAX = modulation maximum dimension

8. If desired, repeat the intermodulation measurement at various settings of the amplifier gain and tone controls.

10-5-4. Checking Distortion by Square-Wave Analysis

The procedure for checking distortion by means of square waves is essentially the same as for sine waves, as described in Sec. 10-5-1. Distortion analysis is more effective with square waves because of their high odd-harmonic content and because it is easier to see a deviation from a straight line with sharp corners, than from a curving line. As in the case of sine wave distortion testing, square waves are introduced into the amplifier input, while the output is monitored on an oscilloscope. The primary concern is deviation of the amplifier (or stage) output waveform from the input waveform (which is also monitored on the oscilloscope). If the oscilloscope has the dual-trace feature, the input and output can be monitored simultaneously. If there is a change in waveform, the nature of the change will often reveal the cause of distortion. For example, poor high-frequency response will round the trailing edge of the output square wave, as shown in Fig. 10-6.

The third, fifth, seventh, and ninth harmonics of a clean square wave are emphasized. Therefore, if an amplifier passes a given audio frequency

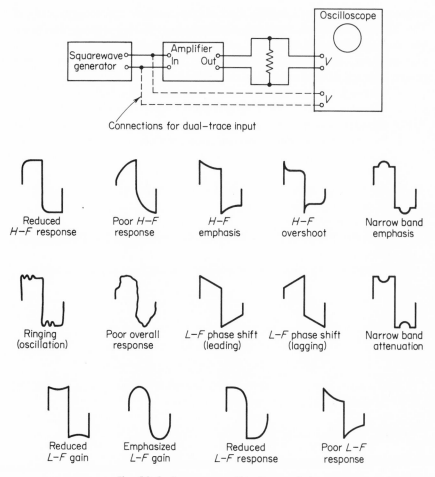

Fig. 10-6. Square-wave distortion analysis.

and produces a clean square-wave output, it is safe to assume that the frequency response is good up to at least nine times the fundamental frequency. For example, if an amplifier passes a clean square wave at 3000 Hz, it shows a good response up to 27 kHz, which is beyond the top limit of the audio range.

In any form of distortion analysis using square waves, the square wave must be clean. (Refer to Chapter 11 for an analysis of pulse characteristics.)

1. Connect the equipment as shown in Fig. 10-6. A load resistor R_1 must be used for power amplifiers and should have a value equal to the amplifier's output impedance.

2. Place the oscilloscope in operation (Chapter 5). Switch on the internal recurrent sweep. Set the sweep selector and sync selector to internal.

3. Set the amplifier amplitude and tone controls to their normal operating point, or at the particular setting specified in the manufacturer's test data.

4. Place the generator in operation as described in its instruction manual. Set the generator output frequency to 1000 Hz or as specified in the amplifier manufacturer's test data. If no data are available, increase the generator output until the waveform no longer increases in amplitude and/or shows distortion. Then reduce the generator output until the waveform shows no distortion.

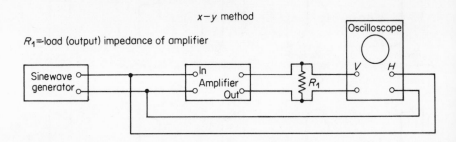

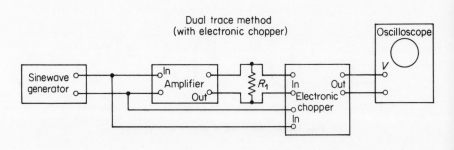

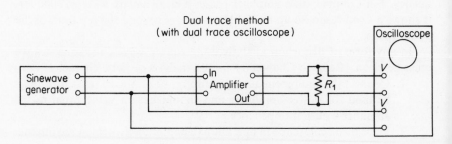

Fig. 10-7. Measuring amplifier phase shift.

5. If necessary, adjust the sweep frequency controls to display one (or possibly two) cycles on the screen.
6. Compare the amplifier output waveform with the input (generator output) waveform. If the output is identical to the input, except possibly for amplitude, there is no distortion. If the output is not identical, compare it with the typical response patterns of Fig. 10-6.
7. If desired, repeat the square-wave distortion analysis at other settings of the amplifier gain and tone controls, as well as at other generator frequencies.

10-6. Measuring Amplifier Phase Shift

An amplifier can be checked for phase shift between input and output by either of the methods described in Chapter 7 (Sec. 7-8, 7-9). The test connection diagrams are shown in Fig. 10-7.

CHAPTER **11**

Checking
Communications Equipment

The role of an oscilloscope in testing communications equipment is often overlooked. The TV bench service technician finds the oscilloscope almost indispensable, but the technician who services communications receivers tends to avoid the oscilloscope. When, however, it is realized that an oscilloscope can provide an effective instrument for AM front end and i-f alignment, FM front end, i-f, and detector alignment, as well as a modulation meter for testing transmitters, the communications service technician can put the oscilloscope in its true perspective.

11-1. Checking Microphones

A microphone can be checked for distortion and frequency response using an oscilloscope. Distortion is checked by applying a sine wave to a loudspeaker placed near the microphone, and monitoring the microphone output on an oscilloscope. Frequency response is checked in essentially the same way, by varying the sine wave over the desired test range of the microphone.
   1. Connect the equipment as shown in Fig. 11-1.
   2. Place the oscilloscope in operation (Chapter 5). Switch on the internal recurrent sweep. Set the sweep selector and sync selector to internal.
   3. Place the generator and amplifier (if any) in operation as described

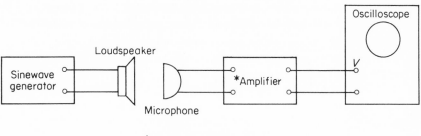

*Amplifier may be omitted
if oscilloscope vertical
gain is sufficient

Fig. 11-1. Checking microphones with an oscilloscope.

in their instruction manuals. Set the generator output frequency to the low limit of the microphone. Adjust the generator and amplifier controls for a suitable pattern on the oscilloscope.

4. Check the oscilloscope pattern for distortion. If there is doubt as to the origin of any observed distortion, temporarily connect the generator output to the amplifier input. If distortion is removed, the cause is in the microphone (assuming that the loudspeaker is distortion-free).

NOTE

For the most accurate results, the microphone should be shielded from all sound sources, except the loudspeaker.

5. Without changing the generator output amplitude, vary the generator frequency over the entire test range of the microphone. Check for any change in amplitude on the oscilloscope pattern.

NOTE

A response curve can be made for the microphone by following the procedures of Sec. 10-2.

11-2. Checking Transmitter Amplitude Modulation with an Oscilloscope

An oscilloscope can be used to display the carrier of an amplitude-modulated radio wave. The percentage of modulation can be calculated from the dimensions of the modulation pattern.

1. Connect the equipment as shown in Fig. 11-2.

NOTE

If the vertical channel response is capable of handling the transmitter output frequency, the output can be applied through the oscilloscope vertical amplifier. If not, the transmitter output must be applied directly to the vertical deflection plates of the oscilloscope CRT.

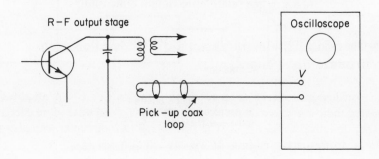

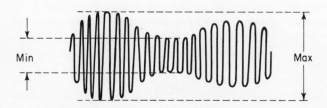

$$\text{Modulation } (\%) = 100 \times \left(\frac{max - min}{max + min} \right)$$

Fig. 11-2. Checking transmitter amplitude modulation with an oscilloscope.

2. Place the oscilloscope in operation (Chapter 5). Switch on the internal recurrent sweep. Set the sweep selector and sync selector to internal. Adjust the horizontal and vertical gain controls for a no-signal trace.
3. Place the transmitter in operation as described in the instruction manual. Initially, set the transmitter for an unmodulated carrier output.
4. Amplitude modulate the transmitter with a sine-wave signal and check the oscilloscope pattern.
5. If necessary, adjust the sweep frequency controls to display a few cycles on the screen.
6. Measure the vertical dimensions MAX and MIN (Fig. 11-2) in screen divisions.
7. Calculate the percentage of modulation using the equation:

$$M(\%) = 100 \left[\frac{\text{MAX} - \text{MIN}}{\text{MAX} + \text{MIN}} \right]$$

where $M(\%)$ = percentage of modulation

MIN = modulation minimum dimension

MAX = modulation maximum dimension

11-3. Checking Transmitter Amplitude Modulation with Trapezoidal Patterns

An oscilloscope can be used to display the carrier of an amplitude-modulated radio wave as a trapezoidal pattern. This method is more effective than that described in Sec. 11-2. The percentage of modulation can also be calculated from the dimensions of the modulation pattern.

1. Connect the equipment as shown in Fig. 11-3.

NOTE

Do not use the oscilloscope amplifiers. Make both the horizontal and vertical connections directly to the oscilloscope CRT.

2. Place the oscilloscope in operation (Chapter 5). Switch off the internal recurrent sweep. Set the sync selector to external. The no-signal trace should appear as a dot at the screen center.
3. Place the transmitter in operation as described in the instruction manual. Initially, set the transmitter for an unmodulated carrier output. This should produce a pattern as shown in Fig. 11-3b.
4. Amplitude modulate the transmitter with a sine-wave signal, and check the oscilloscope pattern. Figure 11-3c, d, and e show typical patterns for 50 per cent modulation, 90–95 per cent modulation, and overmodulation (over 100 per cent), respectively.

NOTE

Adjust the oscilloscope display width with resistor R_1. The height of the oscilloscope display is adjusted by varying the coupling between the pick-up coil and the output tank.

5. Observe the oscilloscope display for signs of nonlinearity. The straightness of the sides of the trapezoidal pattern indicates the modulation linearity. The trapezoidal pattern has one advantage; nonlinearity can be checked quickly.
6. Measure the vertical dimensions (MAX and MIN) (Fig. 11-3f) in screen divisions.
7. Calculate the percentage of modulation using the equation:

$$M(\%) = 100 \left[\frac{\text{MAX} - \text{MIN}}{\text{MAX} + \text{MIN}} \right]$$

where $M(\%)$ = percentage of modulation
          MIN = modulation minimum dimension
          MAX = modulation maximum dimension

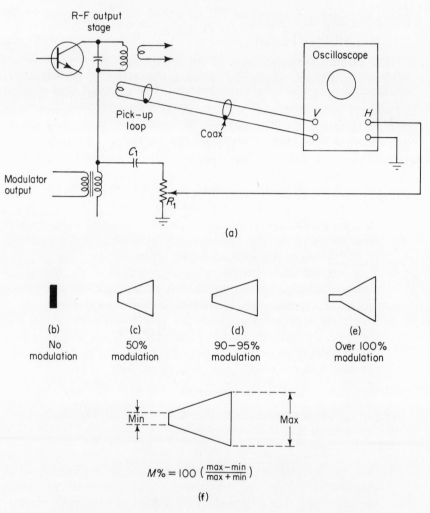

Fig. 11-3. Checking transmitter amplitude modulation with trapezoidal patterns.

11-4. Checking Transmitter Modulator Channels with an Oscilloscope

The modulator channel of a transmitter is essentially an audio amplifier. As such, the modulation channel can be checked for frequency response, power output, noise and hum, distortion, and phase shift as described in Chapter 10. An oscilloscope can also be used as an audio signal tracer for the modulator channel.

11-5. Checking Transmitter RF Channel for Frequency Multiplication with an Oscilloscope

The various multiplier stages of the RF channel in a transmitter must be tuned to different frequencies, which are multiples of the fundamental or oscillator. Although it is possible to tune each multiplier with the aid of a frequency meter, there may be some confusion since most frequency meters respond to harmonics. This confusion of harmonics can be especially difficult when the transmitter is first placed in operation. An oscilloscope can be used to insure that each stage is at the desired frequency, and not at an undesired harmonic. This is done by displaying the stage signals as Lissajous patterns, with the oscillator or fundamental as the reference signal.

1. Connect the equipment as shown in Fig. 11-4.

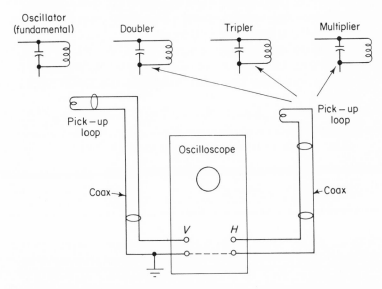

Fig. 11-4. Checking transmitter RF channel for frequency multiplication with an oscilloscope.

NOTE

Do not use the oscilloscope amplifiers. Make both the horizontal and vertical connections directly to the oscilloscope CRT.

2. Place the oscilloscope in operation (Chapter 5). Switch off the internal recurrent sweep. Set the sync selector to external.

3. Place the transmitter in operation as described in the instruction manual. Set the transmitter for an unmodulated carrier output.
4. In turn, connect the horizontal channel to the tank circuit of each stage to be measured. Leave the vertical channel connected to the oscillator (fundamental) tank.
5. Check whether the stage is passing the fundamental, or multiplying (doubling, tripling, or quadrupling, etc.) the fundamental. The stages can be checked at all multiples using the Lissajous patterns, as described in Sec. 7-4.
6. If necessary, adjust the stage tuning circuit until the desired pattern is obtained and stands still.

11-6. Alignment of AM and FM I-F Amplifiers with an Oscilloscope

The response characteristics of AM and FM receiver i-f amplifiers can be checked, or the i-f stages can be aligned, using a sweep generator/oscilloscope combination, as described in Chapter 8. The sweep generator must be capable of sweeping over the entire i-f range. If maximum accuracy is desired, a marker generator must also be used.

1. Connect the equipment as shown in Fig. 11-5.
2. Place the oscilloscope in operation (Chapter 5). Switch off internal recurrent sweep. Set. the oscilloscope sweep selector and sync selector to external.
3. Place the sweep generator in operation as described in its instruction manual. Switch sweep generator blanking control on or off as desired. Adjust the sweep generator to cover the complete i-f range. Usually, AM i-f center frequency is 455 kHz and requires a sweep of about 30 kHz wide; FM i-f center frequency is 10.7 MHz and requires a sweep of about 300 kHz.
4. Check the i-f response curve appearing on the oscilloscope against those of Fig. 11-5, or against the receiver specifications.
5. If it is desired to determine the exact frequencies at which i-f response occurs, the marker generator can be adjusted until the marker pip is aligned at the point of interest. The frequency, or band of frequencies, can be read from the marker generator frequency dial.
6. The amplitude of any point on the response curve can be measured directly on the oscilloscope (assuming that the vertical system is voltage calibrated).
7. Adjust the i-f alignment controls to produce the desired response curve, as specified in the receiver service data.

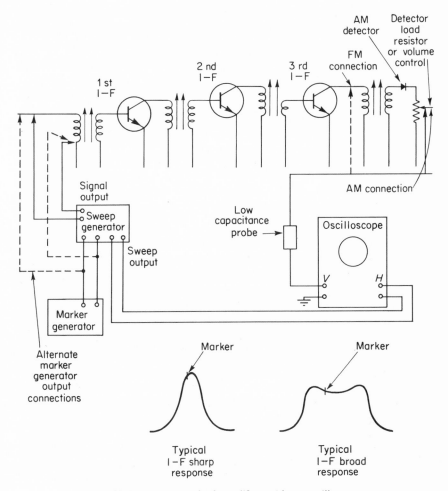

Fig. 11-5. Alignment of i-f amplifiers with an oscilloscope.

11-7. Alignment of AM and FM Front End with an Oscilloscope

The response characteristics of AM and FM receiver RF stages (RF amplifier, mixer or first detector, oscillator) or "front end" can be checked, or aligned, using a sweep generator/oscilloscope combination, as described in Chapter 8. The procedure is essentially the same as for i-f alignment (Sec. 11-6) except that the sweep generator output is connected to the antenna input of the receiver, whereas the input to the first detector or mixer is applied to the oscilloscope vertical channel. The sweep generator must be capable of sweeping over the entire RF range. If maximum accuracy is desired, a marker generator must also be used.

1. Connect the equipment as shown in Fig. 11-6.

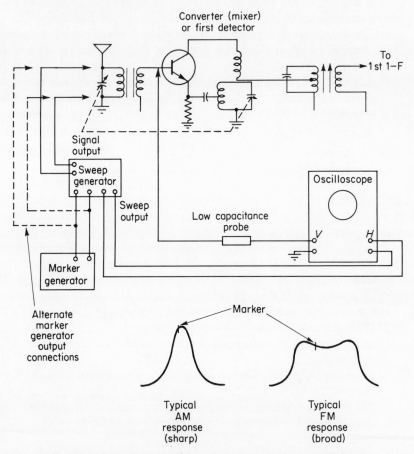

Fig. 11-6. Alignment of RF (front end) stages with an oscilloscope.

2. Place the oscilloscope in operation (Chapter 5). Switch off internal recurrent sweep. Set the oscilloscope sweep selector and sync selector to external.

3. Place the sweep generator in operation as described in its instruction manual. Switch sweep generator blanking control on or off as desired. Adjust the sweep generator to cover the complete RF range. The center frequency depends upon the receiver. Usually, an AM receiver requires a 30 kHz sweep width, and an FM receiver needs about 300 kHz.

4. Check the RF response curve appearing on the oscilloscope against those of Fig. 11-6, or against the receiver specifications.

5. If it is desired to determine the exact frequency at which RF response occurs, the marker generator can be adjusted until the marker pip is aligned at the point of interest. The frequency, or band of frequencies, can be read from the marker generator frequency dial.

6. The amplitude of any point of the response curve can be measured directly on the oscilloscope (assuming that the vertical system is voltage-calibrated).

7. Adjust the RF alignment controls to produce the desired response curve, as specified in the receiver service data. Usually, the RF response of an AM receiver is similar to that of Fig. 11-6b whereas an FM receiver has a broad response similar to that of Fig. 11-6c.

11-8. Alignment of FM Detector with an Oscilloscope

The detector of an FM receiver (either discriminator or ratio detector) can be aligned using the sweep generator/oscilloscope combination. The test connections are similar to front end and i-f alignment. The sweep generator output is connected to the last i-f stage input, whereas the oscilloscope vertical channel is connected across the FM detector load resistor. The sweep generator must be capable of sweeping over the entire i-f range. If maximum accuracy is desired, a marker generator must also be used.

1. Connect the equipment as shown in Fig. 11-7.

2. Place the oscilloscope in operation (Chapter 5). Switch off internal recurrent sweep. Set the oscilloscope sweep selector and sync selector to external.

3. Place the sweep generator in operation as described in its instruction manual. Switch sweep generator blanking control on or off as desired. Set the sweep generator frequency to the receiver intermediate frequency (usually 10.7 MHz). Adjust the sweep width to about 300 kHz.

4. Check the detector response curve appearing on the oscilloscope against that of Fig. 11-7b, or against the receiver specifications.

5. Adjust the last i-f stage and detector alignment controls so that peaks 2 and 4 of the response curve are equal in amplitude above and below the zero line. Also, points 1, 3, and 5 of the response curve should be on the zero reference line.

6. If it is desired to determine the exact frequency at which detector response occurs, the marker generator can be adjusted until the marker pip is aligned at the point of interest. The frequency, or band of frequencies, can be read from the marker generator frequency dial.

7. The amplitude of any point on the response curve can be measured

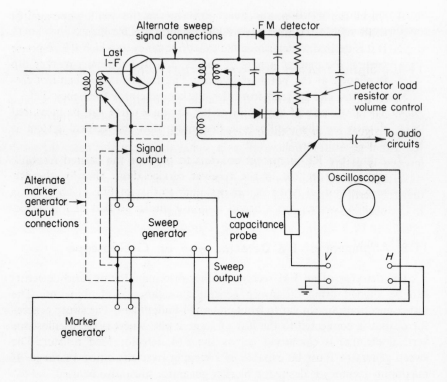

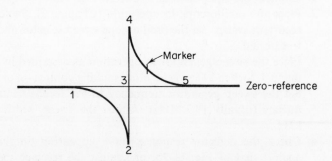

Fig. 11-7. Alignment of FM detector with an oscilloscope.

directly on the oscilloscope (assuming that the vertical system is voltage-calibrated).

11-9. Checking Receiver Audio Channels with an Oscilloscope

The audio channel of a receiver is essentially an audio amplifier. As such, the audio channel can be checked for frequency response, power output, noise and hum, distortion, and phase shift, as described in Chapter 10. An oscilloscope can also be used as an audio signal tracer for the audio channel.

11-10. Signal-tracing Receiver Circuits with an Oscilloscope

Since the sweep generator/oscilloscope combination provides complete alignment of the RF, i-f and detector stages, the same combination can be used as signal tracer for these stages. An oscilloscope can be used with an RF signal generator (nonsweep) as a signal tracer. In this case, the oscilloscope is acting essentially as a voltmeter that also displays the signal waveform. An oscilloscope can be used to signal trace any stage, provided that the vertical channel of the oscilloscope will pass the frequency range. If the oscilloscope frequency range is too narrow, a demodulator or RF probe can be used. In that event, the reference signal applied to the receiver must be modulated.

CHAPTER **12**

Checking Industrial Equipment, Components, and Quantities

The oscilloscope has become the "eyes and ears" of the industrial laboratory technician. Confronted with the problem of checking physical quantities or performance testing, he finds no substitute for a high-quality oscilloscope. This chapter deals with the tests and procedures where a precision laboratory oscilloscope is usually required. Many of the tests can be performed with relatively simple oscilloscopes. The tests and procedures of this chapter have been selected after repeated screening of material. Resourceful laboratory technicians can adapt many of the basic procedures to other uses.

12-1. General Pulse and Square Wave Measurement Techniques

The great majority of industrial oscilloscope applications involve the measurement of pulses and square waves. For that reason, the following sections review pulse measurement techniques, as well as pulse characteristics.

12-1-1. Pulse Definitions

The following terms are commonly used in describing pulse characteristics. The same terms are used with square waves. The terms are illustrated as applied in Fig. 12-1. The input pulse represents an ideal input
waveform for comparison. The other waveforms in Fig. 12-1 represent

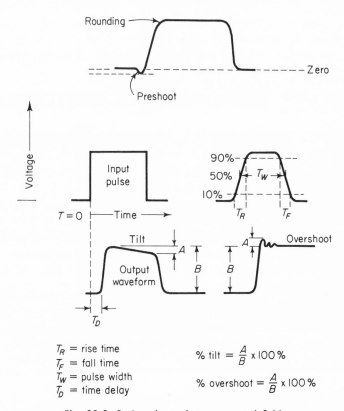

T_R = rise time
T_F = fall time
T_W = pulse width
T_D = time delay

% tilt $= \dfrac{A}{B} \times 100\%$

% overshoot $= \dfrac{A}{B} \times 100\%$

Fig. 12-1. Basic pulse and squarewave definitions.

typical output waveforms in order to show the relationships. The terms are
defined as follows:

Rise time, T_R: The time interval during which the amplitude of the
output voltage changes from 10 per cent to 90 per cent of the rising portion
of the pulse.

Fall time T_F: The time interval during which the amplitude of the output voltage changes from 90 per cent to 10 per cent of the falling portion of the waveform.

Pulse width (*or duration*), T_W: The time duration of the pulse measured between the 50 per cent amplitude levels of the rising and falling portions of the waveform.

Time delay, T_D: The time interval between the beginning of the input pulse ($T = 0$), and the time when the rising portion of the output pulse attains an arbitrary amplitude of 10 per cent above the baseline.

Tilt: A measure of the tilt of the full amplitude; flat-top portion of a pulse. The tilt measurement is usually expressed as a percentage of the amplitude of the rising portion of the pulse.

Overshoot: A measure of the overshoot occurring generally above the 100 per cent amplitude level. This measurement is also expressed as a percentage of the pulse rise.

These definitions are only guides. When the actual pulses are very irregular (such as excessive tilt, overshoot, etc.), the definitions may become ambiguous. In such cases, a more complete description of the pulse will probably be necessary.

12-1-2. Rule of Thumb for Rise-Time Measurements

Since rise-time measurements are of special importance in pulse testing, the relationship between the oscilloscope rise time, and the rise time of the device under test must be taken into account. Obviously, the accuracy of rise-time measurements can be no greater than the rise time of the oscilloscope. Also, if the device is tested by means of an external pulse from a pulse generator, the rise time of the pulse generator must also be taken into account.

For example, if an oscilloscope with a 20-nanosecond rise time is used to measure the rise time of a 15-nanosecond device, the measurements would be hopelessly inaccurate. If a 20-nanosecond pulse generator and a 15-nanosecond oscilloscope were used to measure the rise time of a device, the fastest rise time for accurate measurement would be something greater than 20 nanoseconds. Two basic rules of thumb can be applied to rise-time measurements.

The first method is known as the *root of the sum of the squares*. It involves finding the squares of all the rise times associated with the test, adding these squares together, and then finding the square root of this sum. For example, using the 20-nanosecond pulse generator and the 15-nanosecond oscilloscope, the calculation would be as follows:

$$20 \times 20 = 400; \quad 15 \times 15 = 225; \quad 400 + 225 = 625$$
$$\sqrt{625} = 25 \text{ (nanoseconds)}$$

This means that the fastest possible rise time capable of measurement is 25 nanoseconds.

One major drawback to this rule is that the coaxial cables required to interconnect the test equipment are subject to "skin effect." As frequency increases, the signals tend to travel on the outside or skin of the conductor. This decreases conductor area, and increases resistance. In turn, this increases cable loss. The losses of cables do not add properly to apply the root-sum-squares method, except as an approximation.

The second rule or method states that if the equipment or signal being measured has a rise time *10 times* slower than the test equipment, the error is 1 per cent. This amount is small and can be considered as negligible. If the equipment being measured has a rise time *3 times* slower than the test equipment, the error is slightly less than 6 per cent. By keeping these relationships in mind, the results can be interpreted intelligently.

12-1-3. Maching Pulse Generator Impedance to Device under Test

One problem often encountered when testing pulsed equipment is the matching of impedances. To provide a smooth transition between devices of different characteristic impedance, each device must encounter a total impedance equal to its own characteristic impedance. A certain amount of signal attenuation is usually required to achieve this transition. A simple resistive impedance-matching network that provides minimum attenuation is shown in Fig. 12-2, together with the applicable equations.

For example, to match a 50-ohm system to a 125-ohm system,

$$Z_1 = 50 \text{ ohms} \qquad \text{and} \qquad Z_2 = 125 \text{ ohms}$$

Therefore:

$$R_1 = \sqrt{125(125 - 50)} = 96.8 \text{ ohms}$$

$$R_2 = 50\sqrt{\frac{125}{125 - 50}} = 64.6 \text{ ohms}$$

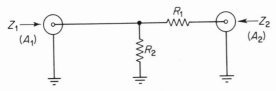

To match impedances: $R_1 = \sqrt{Z_2(Z_2 - Z_1)}$ $R_2 = Z_1\sqrt{\dfrac{Z_2}{Z_2 - Z_1}}$

Voltage attenuation seen from Z_1 end (A_1): $A_1 = \dfrac{R_1}{Z_2} + 1$

Voltage attenuation seen from Z_2 end (A_2): $A_2 = \dfrac{R_1}{R_2} + \dfrac{R_1}{Z_1} + 1$

Fig. 12-2. Resistive impedance matching network for pulse circuits.

Though the network in Fig. 12-2 provides minimum attenuation for a purely resistive impedance-matching device, the attenuation as seen from one end does not equal that seen from the other end. A signal applied from the lower-impedance source (Z_1) encounters a voltage attenuation (A_1) that may be determined as follows:

Assume that R_1 is 96.8 ohms and Z_2 is 125 ohms.

$$A_1 = \frac{96.8}{125} + 1 = 1.77 \text{ attenuation}$$

A signal applied from the higher-impedance source (Z_2) will produce an even greater voltage attenuation (A_2) that may be determined as follows:

Assume that $R_1 = 96.8$ ohms, $R_2 = 64.6$ ohms, and impedance $Z_1 = 50$ ohms.

$$A_2 = \frac{96.8}{64.6} + \frac{96.8}{50} + 1 = 4.44 \text{ attenuation}$$

12-2. Measurement of Pulse Time with External Timing Pulses

On those oscilloscopes where the horizontal sweep circuits are calibrated in units of time, pulse width (duration) or spacing between pulses can be measured directly by counting the number of screen divisions along the horizontal axis. This method is described in Chapter 7, as is the method for converting frequency-calibrated horizontal sweeps to time-calibrated sweeps (Secs. 7-1, 7-2, and 7-3).

It is also possible to use an external *time-mark generator* to calibrate the horizontal scale of an oscilloscope for time measurement. A time-mark generator produces a pulse-type timing wave which is a series of sharp spikes, spaced at precise time intervals. These pulses are applied to the vertical input and appear as a wavetrain as shown in Fig. 12-3. The oscilloscope horizontal gain and positioning controls are adjusted to align the timing spikes with screen lines, until the screen divisions equal the timing pulses. The

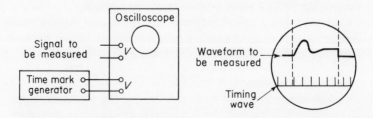

Fig. 12-3. Typical connections and pattern for time measurement with external timing pulses.

accuracy of the oscilloscope timing circuits is then of no concern, since the horizontal channel is calibrated against the external time-mark generator. The timing pulses can be removed, and the signal to be measured applied to the vertical input, provided that the horizontal gain and positioning controls are not touched. Duration or time is read from the calibrated screen divisions in the normal manner. If the oscilloscope has a dual-trace feature, the time-mark generator can be connected to one vertical input; the other vertical input receives the signal to be measured. The two traces can be superimposed, or aligned, whichever is convenient.

Time-mark generators are used for many reasons, but their main advantages are greater accuracy and resolution. For example, a typical time-mark generator unit will produce timing signals at intervals of 10, 1, and 0.1 microseconds.

12-3. Measurement of Pulse Delay

The time interval (or delay) between an input pulse and output pulse introduced by a delay line, digital circuit, multivibrator, or similar circuit, can be measured on an oscilloscope with dual trace. It the delay is exceptionally short, the screen divisions can be calibrated with an external time-mark generator. If the oscilloscope has three vertical inputs, the timing wave from the time-mark generator can be displayed simultaneously with the input and output pulses.

1. Connect the equipment as shown in Fig. 12-4.
2. Place the oscilloscope in operation (Chapter 5). Switch on the internal recurrent sweep. Set the sweep selector and sync selector to internal.
3. Switch on the delay device, if it is powered.
4. Switch on the time-mark generator and pulse generator as described in their instruction manuals.
5. If the oscilloscope is a multiple-trace instrument, set the sweep frequency and sync controls for a single, stationary input pulse and output pulse as shown in Fig. 12-4.
6. Set the horizontal and vertical gain controls and pulse generator output for desired pulse pattern width and height.
7. Count the timing spikes between the input and output pulses to determine the delay interval. Count the timing spikes between the beginning and end of each pulse to determine pulse width or duration.

NOTE

If the oscilloscope is a dual-trace instrument, the screen divisions must be calibrated against the time-mark generator as described in Sec. 12-2. The time-mark generator can then be removed and the input and output pulses applied to the two vertical channels.

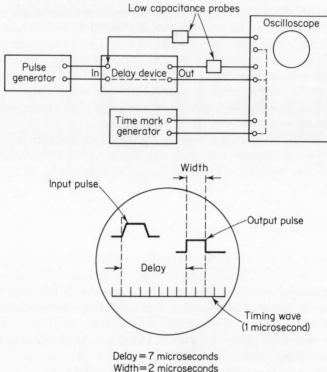

Delay = 7 microseconds
Width = 2 microseconds

Fig. 12-4. Measurement of pulse delay.

12-4. Measuring Impedance with a Pulse Generator and Oscilloscope

A pulse generator/oscilloscope combination can be used to measure impedance of an unknown device by comparison of the reflected pulse with the incident pulse.

1. Connect the equipment as shown in Fig. 12-5.
2. Place the oscilloscope in operation (Chapter 5). Switch on the internal recurrent sweep. Set the sweep selector and sync selector to internal.
3. Switch on the pulse generator as described in its instruction manual. Set the sweep frequency and sync controls to display the output pulse, and the first reflected pulse.

NOTE

This impedance measurement method is based on the comparison of reflected pulses with output pulses. As a signal travels down a transmission line, each time it encounters a mismatch or different

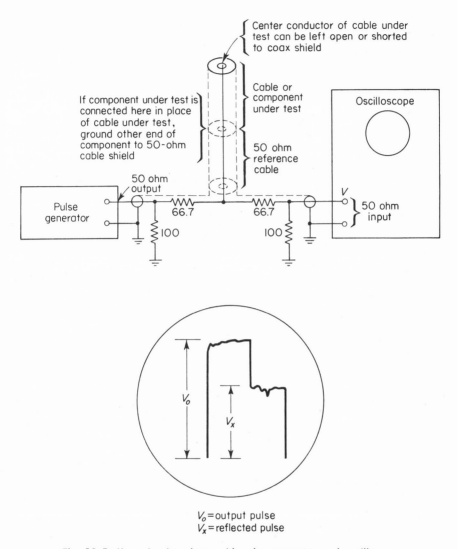

V_o=output pulse
V_x=reflected pulse

Fig. 12-5. Measuring impedance with pulse generator and oscilloscope (using output and reflected pulses).

impedance, a reflection is generated and sent back along the line to the source. The amplitude and polarity of the reflection are determined by the value of the impedance encountered in relation to the characteristic impedance of the cable. If the mismatch impedance is higher than that of the line, the reflection will be of the same polarity as the applied signal; if it is lower than that of the line, the reflection will be of opposite polarity. The reflected signal is added to or subtracted from the amplitude of the pulse if it returns to the source before the pulse has ended. Thus, for a cable with an open end (no termination), the impedance is infinite and the pulse amplitude would be doubled. For a cable with a shorted end, the impedance is zero and the pulse would be canceled.

4. Observe the output and reflected pulses on the oscilloscope screen. Using Fig. 12-5 as a guide, determine the values of V_o (output voltage amplitude) and V_x (reflected voltage amplitude).

5. Calculate the unknown impedance using the following equation:

$$Z = \frac{50}{(2V_o/V_x) - 1}$$

where $Z =$ unknown impedance

$\quad\quad 50 =$ reference impedance (50-ohm coax line)

$\quad\quad V_o =$ peak amplitude produced by the 50-ohm reference impedance

$\quad\quad V_x =$ peak amplitude at the time of the reflection

12-5. Measuring Strain with an Oscilloscope

An oscilloscope provides a reliable means of measuring dynamic strain (where strain changes rapidly with time). Static strain (where the strain remains constant) can be measured easily with strain gauges connected in a bridge circuit. When the strain varies over a short time span, the simple bridge circuit cannot record this action, as an oscilloscope can. Because of the instantaneous nature of the trace, the display should be photographed (unless a storage-type oscilloscope is used).

As shown in Fig. 12-6, the strain gauges are connected in a bridge circuit, the output of which is applied to the oscilloscope vertical channel. The bridge is balanced under no-strain conditions with potentiometer R_1. One strain gauge is placed on the material or structure to be tested; the other identical strain gauge is used as a reference. The oscilloscope is not deflected when the bridge is balanced (no-strain). When the material or structure is stressed, the resistance of the attached strain gauge is changed. This unbalances the bridge and produces a d-c output that is proportional to the change. The d-c output deflects the oscilloscope vertical trace, and produces a plot of strain versus time. The bridge circuit can be calibrated in terms of strain (microinches of variation per inch-ounces of applied force), or strain versus voltage deflection, or whatever proves convenient for the particular test. The entire trace can be photographed for a permanent record.

1. Connect the equipment as shown in Fig. 12-6.
2. Place the oscilloscope in operation (Chapter 5). Switch on the internal

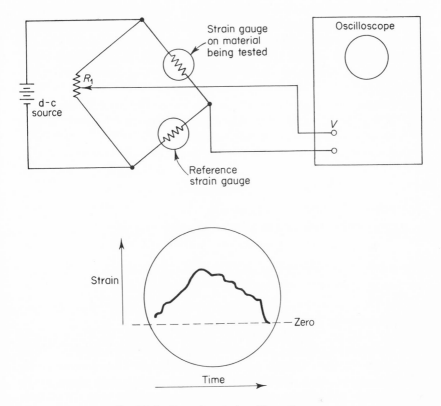

Fig. 12-6. Measuring strain with oscilloscope.

recurrent sweep. Set the sweep selector and sync selector to internal. Use a sweep time interval that will be longer than the strain interval. Set up the oscilloscope camera as necessary.

3. Set the oscilloscope to measure dc. Balance the bridge adjusting potentiometer R_1. The oscilloscope should be at zero vertical deflection with the bridge balanced.

4. Hold the camera shutter open, stress the material or structure under test, close the camera shutter, and develop the picture.

5. Using the developed photo, measure the strain versus time plot. Use a longer sweep time interval if the complete strain plot is not displayed.

12-6. Measuring Acceleration with an Oscilloscope

An oscilloscope will provide a means of measuring variations in acceleration as a function of time. The procedure is almost identical to that of dynamic strain measurement (Sec. 12-5). The major difference is that a resistance-type accelerometer is used in place of the strain gauge (Fig. 12-7).

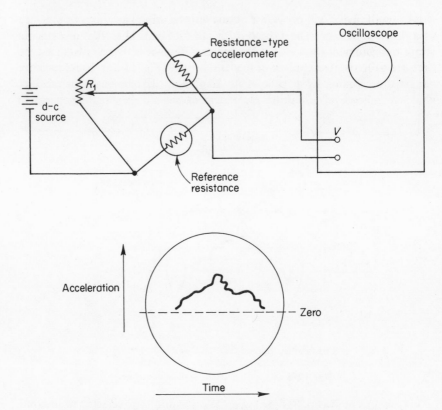

Fig. 12-7. Measuring acceleration with an oscilloscope.

The opposite leg of the bridge is composed of a fixed resistance to match the accelerometer resistance. The bridge is balanced under no-acceleration conditions, or at some preselected value of acceleration by potentiometer R_1. The oscilloscope is not deflected when the bridge is balanced (no acceleration). When the acceleration changes, the accelerometer resistance is changed. This unbalances the bridge and produces a d-c output that is proportional to acceleration change. The d-c output deflects the oscilloscope vertical trace and produces a plot of acceleration change versus time. The bridge can be calibrated in terms of acceleration (feet per second^2 per volt) or whatever is convenient. The entire trace can be photographed for a permanent record. (Set up the equipment as shown in Fig. 12-7, and follow the procedure of Sec. 12-5.)

12-7. Measuring Pressure with an Oscilloscope

An oscilloscope will provide a means of measuring variations in pressure as a function of time. The procedure is almost identical to that of dynamic strain measurement (Sec. 12-5). The major difference is that a resistance-type pressure gauge is used in place of the strain gauge (Fig. 12-8a). These pressure gauges are actuated by a bellows or diaphragm that moves with pressure changes. Bellows or diaphragm movement causes a corresponding change in

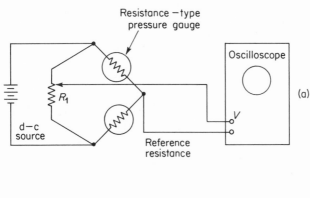

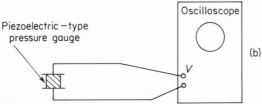

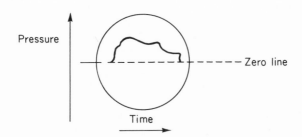

Fig. 12-8. Measuring pressure with an oscilloscope.

resistance. The opposite leg of the bridge is composed of a fixed resistance to match the pressure gauge resistance. The bridge is balanced under no-pressure conditions, or at some preselected value of pressure, by potentiometer R_1. The oscilloscope is not deflected when the bridge is balanced (no pressure). When pressure changes, the pressure gauge resistance changes. This unbalances the bridge and produces a d-c output that is proportional to pressure change. The d-c output deflects the oscilloscope vertical trace and produces a plot of pressure change versus time. The bridge can be calibrated in terms of pressure (pounds per volt) or whatever is convenient.

Pressure is sometimes measured with piezoelectric pressure pickups, as shown in Fig. 12-8b. These pickups are self-generating and do not require a bridge circuit. Piezoelectric pickups are connected directly to the vertical input of the oscilloscope.

Set up the equipment as shown in Fig. 12-8a or 12-8b, and follow the procedure of Sec. 12-5.

12-8. Measuring Electrical Noise with an Oscilloscope

As oscilloscope provides a reliable means of measuring electrical noise or "hash." Such electrical noise can be defined as any undesired, non-repetitive signal present in a circuit, and includes background noise, transient noise, etc. Usually, electrical noise is a combination of many frequencies and waveforms, all of which can be displayed on an oscilloscope. Peak amplitude of the noise is usually of major importance in any test. This can be measured on an oscilloscope in the normal manner. Because of the instantaneous nature of the trace, the display should be photographed (unless a storage-type oscilloscope is used; refer to Sec. 9-11).

As shown in Fig. 12-9, the noise source is connected to the oscilloscope vertical channel. The source can be connected directly to the vertical input, or through a tuned amplifier. The tuned amplifier (such as is found in sound and vibration analyzers, wave analyzers, etc.) is used where noise frequency is of particular importance. If the noise source is a voltage, the vertical input can be connected across a component or branch of the circuit. If the noise appears as a current, a resistance must be inserted in the circuit, and the voltage drop across the resistance measured. If it is not practical to interrupt the circuit, a current probe can be used (Sec. 6-10).

1. Connect the equipment as shown in Fig. 12-9.

NOTE

The tuned amplifier can be omitted if peak noise amplitude is the only factor of interest.

2. Place the oscilloscope in operation (Chapter 5). Switch on the internal

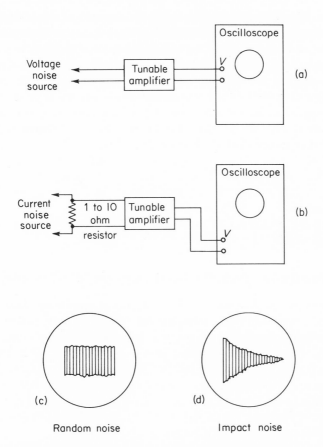

Fig. 12-9. Measuring electrical noise with an oscilloscope.

recurrent sweep. Set the sweep selector and sync selector to internal. Set up the oscilloscope camera as necessary.

3. Set the sweep frequency and horizontal and vertical gain controls to display the noise pattern similar to that of Fig. 12-9c or 12-9d.

4. Measure the peak-to-peak noise amplitude along the voltage-calibrated vertical axis.

5. If the noise pattern appears repetitive, measure the time interval between noise intervals, using the time-calibrated horizontal axis.

6. If impact noise is to be measured and recorded, hold the camera shutter open, initiate the impact, close the camera shutter, and develop the picture. Using the developed photo, measure the peak-to-peak amplitude, as well as the time interval of the impact noise.

7. If it is desired to determine the frequency range of noise signals, tune

the amplifier to each frequency of interest and note the time and amplitude of the noise signals.

12-9. Measuring Acoustic Noise and Sound with an Oscilloscope

The procedure for measuring acoustic noise (or sound) with an oscilloscope is almost identical to that for electrical noise (Sec. 12-8). The major difference is that a microphone is used as the noise pickup, instead of connecting into a circuit to measure noise voltage or current. The microphone acts as a transducer and converts acoustic noise into an electrical signal. Usually a capacitor-type microphone is used, with a preamplifier, for most acoustic noise measurements. Also, the voltage readings on the oscilloscope vertical channel can be converted to decibels, if desired.

Set up the equipment as shown in Fig. 12-10, and follow the procedure of Sec. 12-8.

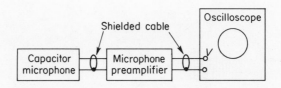

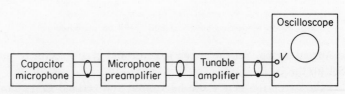

Fig. 12-10. Measuring acoustic noise (or sound) with an oscilloscope.

12-10. Measuring Vibration with an Oscilloscope

The procedure for measuring vibration (continuous, random, or impact) with an oscilloscope is almost identical to that for electrical noise (See. 12-8) or acoustic noise (Sec. 12-9). The major difference is that a vibration pickup is used instead of a microphone. The pickup acts as a transducer and converts vibration into an electrical signal. Most vibration transducers are piezoelectric instruments which produce an a-c voltage proportional to acceleration of the vibrating body. Some vibration transducers contain integration networks which provide output voltages proportional to velocity and displacement. Other vibration transducers are supplied with special preamplifiers. The vibration transducer manufacturers often supply calibration data which permit the voltage readings on the oscilloscope to be converted to a direct readout of velocity, acceleration, displacement, amplitude, etc.

(Set up the equipment as shown in Fig. 12-11 and follow the procedure of Sec. 12-8.)

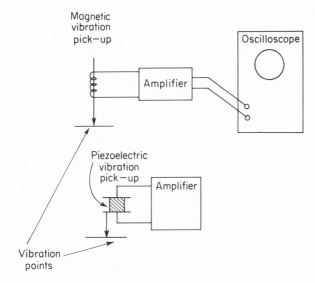

Fig. 12-11. Measuring vibration with an oscilloscope.

12-11. Measurement of Rotational Speed with an Oscilloscope

An oscilloscope can be used to measure rotational speed of machinery. In this application, the oscilloscope functions as an indicating device. The actual rotation is converted to an electrical signal by a transducer. There are three basic types of transducers: magnetic, capacitive, and photoelectric. The magnetic tachometer-type transducer is the most common. Such magnetic transducers are miniature generators driven by the rotating machinery. Usually they produce an a-c output. Some magnetic transducers produce an output voltage proportional to rotational speed and are rated in **RPM** per volt. Other magnetic transducers produce a signal, the frequency of which is proportional to rotational speed. The capacitive and photoelectric transducers are almost always of the frequency type.

12-11-1. Procedure for Frequency-type Speed Transducers

1. Connect the equipment as shown in Fig. 12-12.
2. Place the oscilloscope in operation (Chapter 5). Switch off the internal recurrent sweep. Set the sweep selector and sync selector to external.

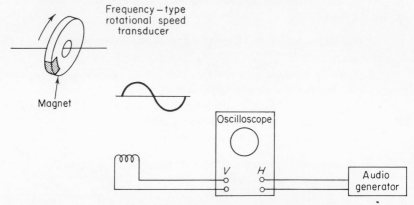

Fig. 12-12. Measuring rotational speed with frequency-type speed transducer.

3. Connect the transducer to the machinery as described in the transducer instruction manual. Usually capacitive and photoelectric transducers do not require direct coupling.
4. Place the audio generator in operation as described in its instruction manual.
5. Adjust the audio generator frequency to obtain a stable pattern on the oscilloscope. Identify the transducer output frequency by means of Lissajous figures, as described in Sec. 7-4.
6. Convert the frequency measurement into a speed indication, using the conversion factor supplied with the transducer.
7. If desired, any of the frequency measurement techniques described in Chapter 7 can be used instead of Lissajous figures.

12-11-2. Procedure for Voltage-type Speed Transducers

1. Connect the equipment as shown in Fig. 12-13.
2. Place the oscilloscope in operation (Chapter 5). Switch on the internal recurrent sweep. Set the sweep selector and sync selector to internal.
3. Connect the transducer to the machinery as described in the transducer instruction manual.

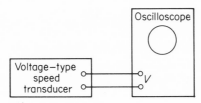

Fig. 12-13. Measuring rotational speed with voltage-type speed transducer.

4. Set the oscilloscope to measure ac or dc, depending upon the transducer output.
5. With the machinery operating, measure the transducer voltage output on the oscilloscope vertical scale.
6. Convert the voltage measurement into a speed indication, using the conversion factor supplied with the transducer.

12-12. Measurement of Thyratron and SCR Conduction Angle with an Oscilloscope

An oscilloscope can be used to measure the conduction angle of a thyratron or an SCR (silicon-controlled rectifier). The oscilloscope must be capable of dual-trace operation. As shown in Fig. 12-14, one trace of the oscilloscope displays the anode current; the other displays the grid (for thyratron) or trigger (for SCR) voltage. Since the grid or trigger is synchronized with anode current, the portion of the grid or trigger cycle in which anode current flows is the conduction angle.

1. Connect the equipment as shown in Fig. 12-14a or 12-14b, as applicable.
2. Place the oscilloscope in operation (Chapter 5). Switch on the internal recurrent sweep. Set the sweep selector and sync selector to internal.
3. Switch on the thyratron or SCR circuit.
4. Adjust the sweep frequency and sync controls to produce two or three stationary cycles of each wave on the screen.
5. On the basis of one uncontrolled condition pulse equalling 180°, determine the angle of flow of anode current, by reference to the grid or trigger voltage trace. For example, in the thyratron display of Fig. 12-14, anode current starts to flow at 90° and stops at 180°, giving a conduction angle of 90°. In the SCR display of Fig. 12-14, anode current starts to flow at 90° and stops at 120°, giving a conduction angle of 30°.

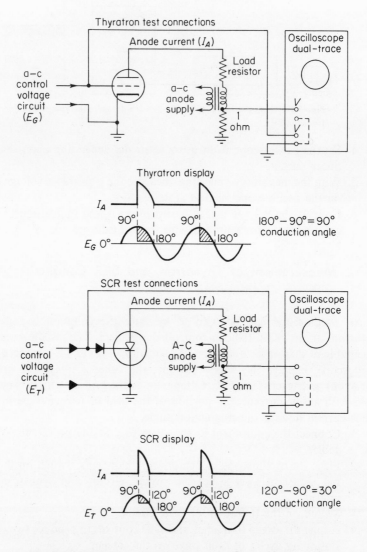

Fig. 12-14. Measurement of thyratron and SCR conduction angle with an oscilloscope.

12-13. Measuring Power Supply Ripple with an Oscilloscope

An oscilloscope provides the only satisfactory means of measuring ripple in power supplies. An oscilloscope will display the ripple waveform from which the amplitude, frequency, and nature of the ripple voltage can be determined. Usually, the oscilloscope is set to the a-c mode when measuring ripple, since this blocks the d-c output of the power supply. Normally, ripple voltage is small in relation to the power supply voltage. Therefore, if the

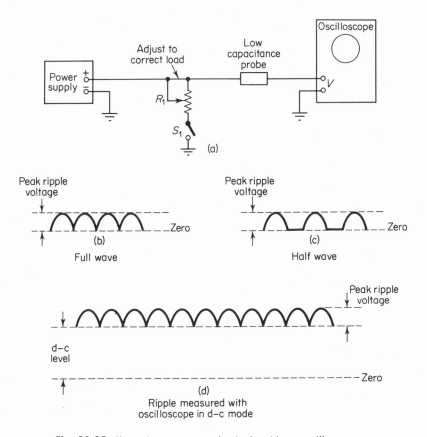

Fig. 12-15. Measuring power supply ripple with an oscilloscope.

oscilloscope gain is set to display the ripple, the power supply d-c voltage would drive the display off screen.

1. Connect the equipment as shown in Fig. 12-15.
2. Place the oscilloscope in operation (Chapter 5). Switch on the internal recurrent sweep. Set the sweep selector and sync selector to internal.
3. Switch on the power supply. If the test is to be made under load conditions, close switch S_1. Open switch S_1 for a no-load test. The value of R_1 must be chosen to provide the power supply with the desired load. Usually, power supply ripple is tested at full load and half load.

NOTE

Make certain that the combined d-c and ripple output of the power supply does not exceed the oscilloscope voltage input rating.

4. Adjust the sweep frequency and sync controls to produce two or three stationary cycles of each wave on the screen.

5. Measure the peak amplitude of the ripple on the voltage-calibrated method described in Chapter 7.

NOTE

When measuring frequency, note that a full-wave power supply (Fig. 12-15b) will produce two ripple "humps" per cycle, whereas a half-wave power supply (Fig. 12-15c) will produce one "hump" per cycle.

6. If the power supply d-c output must be measured simultaneously with the ripple, set the oscilloscope for d-c mode. The baseline should be deflected upward to the d-c level, and the ripple should be displayed at that level (Fig. 12-15d). If this drives the display off screen, reduce the vertical gain using the step-attenuator, and measure the d-c output. Then return the vertical gain to a level where the ripple can be measured and use the vertical position control to bring the display back onto the screen for ripple measurement. This procedure will work with most laboratory oscilloscopes. On shop-type oscilloscopes where the vertical gain control must be set at a given "calibrate" position, the procedure will prove difficult, if not impossible.

7. A study of the ripply waveform can reveal defects in the power supply. For example, if the power supply is unbalanced (one rectifier passing more current than the other), the ripple "humps" will be unequal in amplitude. If there is noise or fluctuation in the power supply, the ripple "humps" will vary in amplitude or shape. If the ripple varies in frequency, the a-c source is varying. If a full-wave power supply produces a half-wave output, one rectifier is not passing current.

12-14. Measuring Commutator Ripple with an Oscilloscope

An oscilloscope can be used to measure commutator ripple of a d-c generator. The procedure is similar to that for measurement of a power supply (Sec. 12-13).

1. Connect the equipment as shown in Fig. 12-16.
2. Place the oscilloscope in operation (Chapter 5). Switch on the internal recurrent sweep. Set the sweep selector and sync selector to internal.
3. Energize the generator. If the test is to be made under load conditions, close switch S_1. Open switch S_1 for a no-load test. The value of R_1 must be chosen to provide the generator with the desired load. Usually, generator ripple is tested at full load and half load.

NOTE

Make certain that the combined d-c and ripple output of the generator does not exceed the oscilloscope voltage input rating.

4. Adjust the sweep frequency and sync controls to produce two or three stationary cycles of each wave on the screen.

5. Measure the peak amplitude of the ripple on the voltage-calibrated vertical axis (Fig. 12-16b). Measure the ripple frequency using the most convenient method described in Chapter 7.

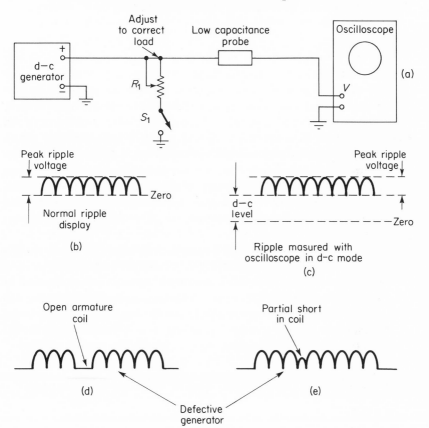

Fig. 12-16. Measuring generator ripple with an oscilloscope.

NOTE

Usually the ripple frequency of a generator is dependent upon the number of armature turns and the armature speed. For example, if the armature has 10 turns and the armature is driven at 10 revolutions per second (600 RPM), the ripple frequency would be 100 Hz.

6. If the generator d-c output must be measured simultaneously with the ripple, set the oscilloscope for d-c mode. The baseline should be deflected upward to the d-c level, and the ripple should be displayed at that level (Fig. 12-16c).

7. A study of the ripple waveform can reveal defects in the generator. For example, if one armature coil is open or shorted, the corresponding ripple "hump" will be missing (Fig. 12-16d). If one armature coil has a loose connection or high-resistance short, the corresponding "hump" will be lower in amplitude. If there is "brush chatter," the ripple "humps" will vary in amplitude or shape.

12-15. Checking Oscillator Circuits with an Oscilloscope

An oscilloscope can provide an excellent means of checking the pulse or square-wave oscillator circuits found in industrial electronic equipment. Such circuits are difficult, if not impossible, to check by any other means. Amplifier and power supply circuits can be checked with a meter, or signal generator and meter combination, but an oscillator or generator output must be monitored as to frequency, amplitude, and waveshape.

It is impossible to describe the procedures for checking each type of oscillator, multivibrator, generator, etc., in this book. The following procedures are applicable to most self-generating circuits and can be adapted to meet the test needs of specific circuits.

1. Connect the equipment as shown in Fig. 12-17. Use a low-capacitance probe for all measurements. The oscilloscope should have a voltage-calibrated vertical axis, and a time-calibrated horizontal axis.
2. Place the oscilloscope in operation (Chapter 5). Switch on the internal recurrent sweep. Set the sweep selector and sync selector to internal.
3. Switch on the oscillator circuit. Touch the low-capacitance probe to the circuit test point. Figure 12-17 shows two typical oscillator circuits and typical waveforms.
4. Adjust the sweep frequency and sync controls to produce two or three stationary cycles of each waveform on the screen.
5. Measure the waveform amplitude of interest on the voltage-calibrated vertical axis.
6. Measure the waveform duration of interest on the time-calibrated horizontal axis.
7. If the horizontal axis is time-calibrated, and it is desired to determine the pulse repetition rate or output frequency, measure the duration of *one complete cycle* (not one pulse), then convert this time duration into frequency as described in Sec. 7-2.
8. If the horizontal axis is frequency calibrated, and it is desired to determine the pulse repetition rate or output frequency, adjust the sweep and sync controls to produce one complete cycle, then convert this into frequency as described in Sec. 7-3.

NOTE

The other frequency measuring techniques of Chapter 7 (Lissajous figures, Z-axis modulation) could be used. A time-calibrated

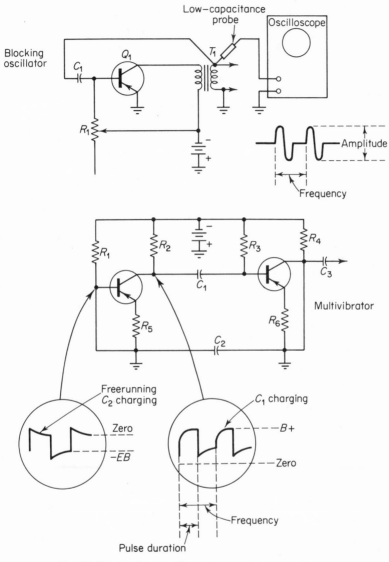

Fig. 12-17. Checking oscillator circuits with an oscilloscope.

horizontal axis is usually the most convenient for measurement of pulse frequencies.

12-16. Using an Oscilloscope in Computer Testing

Because of the high speeds involved in computer testing, an oscilloscope with good transient response and wide passband is about the only instrument capable of monitoring all computer circuits. Of course, the usefulness of an oscilloscope in computer testing depends upon the features or capabilities of the instrument. For example, an oscilloscope with a multitrace capability will permit the two inputs and one output of a typical OR circuit to be monitored simultaneously. A dual-trace oscilloscope can monitor the input and output of a flip-flop circuit simultaneously.

In many cases, the oscilloscope is used in a routine manner when testing computer circuits. For example, voltage and current are measured as described in Chapter 6; time, frequency, and phase are measured as described in Chapter 7. If computer circuit data are nonrepetitive, the data must be photographed (unless a storage oscilloscope is used). The gain of operational amplifiers is measured as described in Chapter 10.

In actual practice, the technician, to use an oscilloscope intelligently, must know exactly what kind of signal should appear at each point in a computer circuit. Operation of computer circuits, as well as the highly specialized techniques of computer service, are beyond the scope of this book. Figures 12-18–12-22 summarize the most common applications of the oscilloscope in computer circuit testing.

Figure 12-18 shows an oscilloscope used to check the input and output of an inverter circuit.

Figure 12-19 shows an oscilloscope used to check the output of a memory unit in relation to the clock pulses.

Figure 12-20 shows an oscilloscope used to check the operation of a flip-flop circuit (used to provide countdown).

Figure 12-21 shows an oscilloscope used to check an OR circuit.

Figure 12-22 shows an oscilloscope used to check an AND circuit.

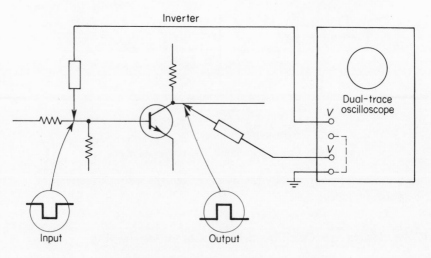

Fig. 12-18. Checking inverter circuit operation.

In all cases, the internal recurrent sweep is used, and the sweep/sync controls are set to display a suitable number of pulses. Although the amplitude and duration (or frequency) of pulses can be measured with the test connections shown, the relationship of pulses (input to output, memory to clock) is the factor of major interest.

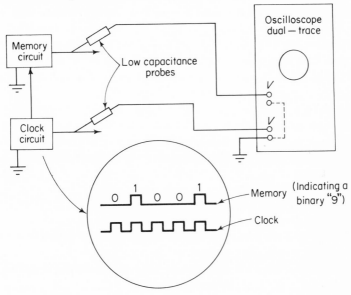

Fig. 12-19. Checking memory and clock circuit operation.

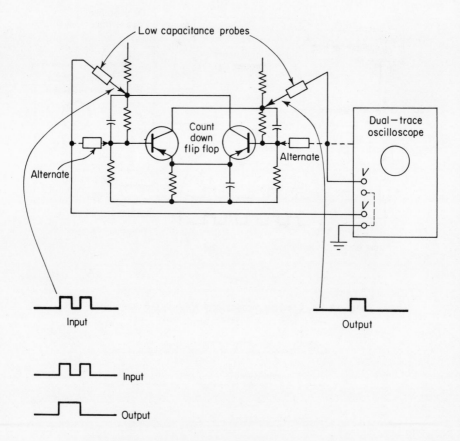

Fig. 12-20. Checking flip-flop (countdown) circuit operation.

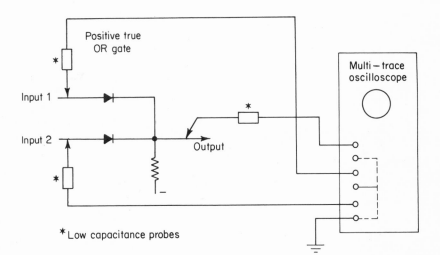

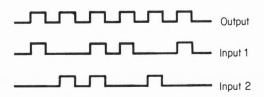

Fig. 12-21. Checking OR circuit operation.

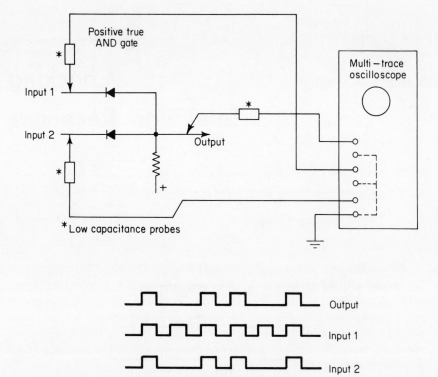

Fig. 12-22. Checking AND circuit operation.

CHAPTER 13

Checking
Television Receivers

An oscilloscope sweep generator/marker generator is the best instrument for testing a black-and-white TV receiver. A color TV receiver requires a color generator. This chapter describes the basic alignment procedures for a black-and-white TV receiver using the oscilloscope/sweep generator combination. Remember that a color TV receiver is essentially a black-and-white set, except for the color display circuits. Therefore the basic alignment procedures are the same.

13-1. Checking Operating Waveforms

An oscilloscope is the best instrument for checking the amplitude, frequency, and waveshape of video and sync pulses in any TV receiver. These waveshapes can be checked without a signal generator of any type, since many of them are generated in the TV receiver itself or are produced by the incoming transmitted TV signal.

1. Connect the equipment as shown in Fig. 13-1. Have a low-capacitance probe and a demodulator probe available.
2. Place the oscilloscope in operation (Chapter 5). Switch on the internal recurrent sweep. For vertical signals, set the sweep frequency and sync controls to 30 Hz. This will display two complete cycles of the wave-

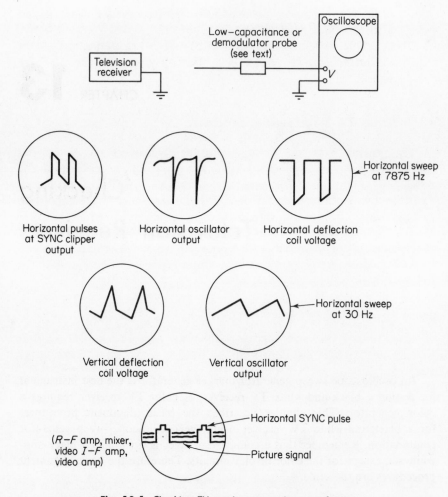

Fig. 13-1. Checking TV receiver operating waveforms.

form. For horizontal signals, set the sweep and sync controls for 7875 Hz. This will also display two complete cycles of the waveform.

NOTE

Many oscilloscopes designed especially for TV service have preset horizontal sweep frequency positions of 30 and 7875 Hz.

3. Switch on the TV receiver, tune in the desired channel, set the contrast, hold, and other receiver controls to their normal operating position.

4. In turn, connect the oscilloscope probe to each point of interest in the TV receiver. Use a demodulator probe for signals in any stage ahead

of the video detector. Use a low-capacitance probe for signals in and after the video detector.

5. Check the waveforms against those of Fig. 13-1 or, preferably, against the manufacturer's service data. The waveforms of Fig. 13-1 are typical.

13-2. Basic TV Alignment Procedure

The general procedure for alignment of split-sound and intercarrier types of television receivers is the same, the major differences being in the number of intermediate frequencies used and the frequencies employed. There are four separate steps for overall alignment: tuner or RF alignment, picture (video) i-f alignment, trap alignment, and sound i-f and FM detector alignment. The actual procedures for these alignments should be followed as described in the manufacturer's service data. The actual response waveforms should be checked against those shown in the service data, using the following basic procedures as a guide.

13-2-1. Tuner Alignment

If the tuner is defective, it is generally better to work with the tuner set to only one channel position until the trouble is corrected. Then, other channel positions can be compared with the initial channel for sensitivity, switching noise, and general performance.

If the tuner is satisfactory in these respects, it is advisable to check the alignment by observing the response curves for each channel. Curves for individual channels should be examined and compared with those shown in the manufacturer's service notes. If a response curve indicates that alignment is required, the technician should refer to the alignment curves given in the service data as guides and follow closely the recommended alignment procedure. Alignment should not be attempted until these preliminary tests have been completed. In principle, complete front-end alignment includes alignment of the antenna input circuits and adjustment of the amplifier and RF oscillator circuits. Most tuners merely require "touch up," in which relatively few of the adjustments are used.

Either way, the adjustments require that a sweep signal and marker signal be fed into the tuner so that a response curve with markers will be reproduced on the oscilloscope screen. Alignment is accomplished by setting adjustments so that the waveshape on the oscilloscope screen resembles the waveshape shown by the manufacturer in the service notes. Signals from the marker generator are used to provide frequency reference points in shaping the curve.

Serious misalignment of the tuner or considerable difficulty or failure in alignment may indicate a defective component. If proper alignment procedure fails to produce correct tuner curves, the technician should check individual components in the RF unit.

The RF tuner can be aligned using either the direct-signal injection method, or with the aid of marker adder units.

NOTE

With the marker adder system of alignment, also known as *post-injection* or *bypass alignment*, the marker signal is added to the sweep response curve by the marker adder unit after the demodulated sweep signal is taken out of the receiver under test. With conventional direct-signal injection method, in which the sweep and marker signals are both passed through the receiver circuits, overloading or clipping by the receiver circuits can introduce distortion of the marker and distortion of the sweep curve by the marker. The marker adder system of adding markers to the response curve eliminates this source of distortion. In addition, the marker adder system permits simple and precise alignment of a variety of trap circuits without marker "suckout."

1. Connect the equipment as shown in Fig. 13-2 for marker adder alignment, or as shown in Fig. 13-3 for direct-signal injection.
2. Place the oscilloscope in operation (Chapter 5). Switch off the internal recurrent sweep. Set the sweep selector and sync selector so that the horizontal sweep is obtained from the generator sweep output. If the generator sweep is at line frequency, the oscilloscope horizontal sweep can be set to line. The phasing control on the oscilloscope or sweep generator must be set to produce a single pattern. (Refer to Chapter 8).
3. Switch on the sweep generator and marker generator as described in their respective instruction manuals.
4. Disable the avc-agc circuits in the receiver under test. Use the bias recommended by the manufacturer's service notes. Usually, this is about −1.5 volt. Make certain to apply the negative bias to the avc-agc line, and the positive bias terminal to the receiver chassis.
5. For marker adder alignment, connect the demodulated sweep pickup lead to the receiver video output.

NOTE

This test point may be across the load resistor of the receiver second detector if an "overall" response curve (RF, i-f, detector) is desired. If the shape of the tuner curve is to be checked, connect the lead to the test point (known as the "looker point") in the tuner mixer circuit. On some tuners, a demodulated signal can be ob-

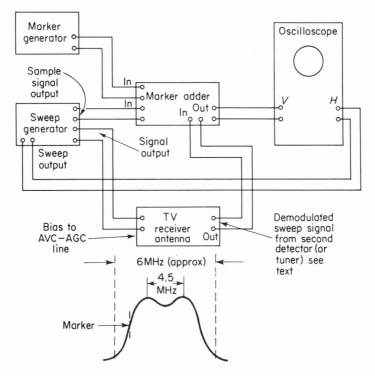

Fig. 13-2. Tuner alignment with marked adder.

tained at this point. However, the oscilloscope should be connected to the point through an isolating resistor (about 50
kilohms). On other tuners, it will be necessary to demodulate the
sweep signal by means of an RF probe. In these cases, the manufacturer's service notes should be consulted for the correct procedure.

6. For direct-injection alignment connect the oscilloscope probe to the
receiver second detector.
7. Adjust the sweep and marker generators to the appropriate channel
frequency. Set sweep width to at least 10 MHz. Adjust the oscilloscope horizontal and vertical gain controls as necessary for a trace
similar to that of Fig. 13-2 or 13-3.

13-2-2. Picture (Video) I-F Alignment

If a television receiver is to give wide-band amplification to the television
signal, the picture i-f (video) system of the receiver must pass a frequency
band of approximately 4 MHz. This is necessary to insure that all the video
information is fed through to the picture tube grid, and the resultant picture

has full definition. The bandpass of color TV receivers must be essentially flat to beyond 4 MHz to insure that color information contained in the color side bands is not lost.

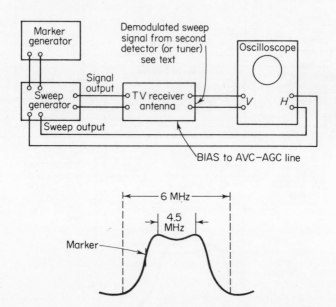

Fig. 13-3. Tuner alignment sweep and marker by direct/injection.

An "overall" i-f response curve may be obtained by feeding the i-f signal into the mixer stage. Markers from the marker generator should also be injected into the mixer stage. Intermediate frequency markers should be used.

The i-f stages can also be checked and aligned, using either the direct-signal injection method, or marker adder units (post-injection or bypass alignment).

1. Connect the equipment as shown in Fig. 13-4 for marker adder alignment, or as shown in Fig. 13-5 for direct-signal injection.
2. Place the oscilloscope in operation (Chapter 5). Switch off the internal recurrent sweep. Set the sweep selector and sync selector so that the horizontal sweep is obtained from the generator sweep output. If the generator sweep is at line frequency, the oscilloscope horizontal sweep can be set to line. The phasing control on the oscilloscope or sweep generator must be set to produce a single pattern. (Refer to Chapter 8.)
3. Switch on the sweep generator and marker generator as described in their instruction manuals.
4. Disable the avc-agc circuits in the receiver under test. Use the bias

recommended by the manufacturer's service notes. Usually this is about −1.5 volt. Make certain to apply the negative bias to the avc-agc line, and the positive bias terminal to the receiver chassis.

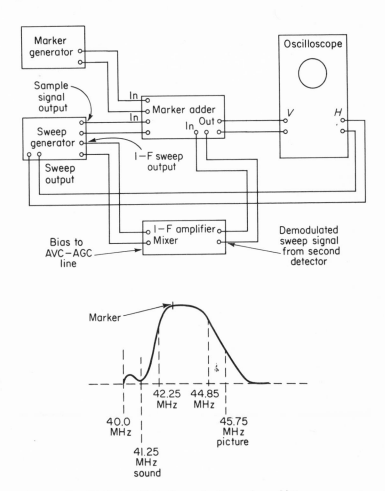

Fig. 13-4. i-f video alignment with marker adder.

5. For marker adder alignment, connect the marker adder demodulated sweep pickup lead to the receiver video output (second detector). For direct-injection alignment, connect the oscilloscope probe to the second detector.
6. Adjust the sweep and marker generators to the appropriate intermediate frequency. Set sweep width to at least 5 MHz. Adjust the oscilloscope horizontal and vertical gain controls as necessary for a trace similar to that of Fig. 13-4 or Fig. 13-5.

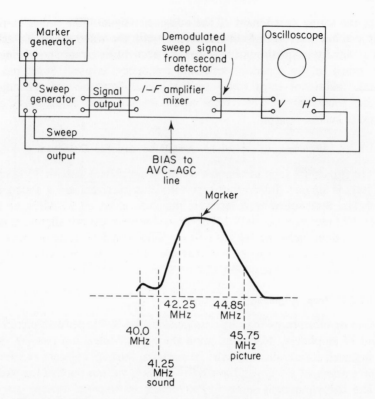

Fig. 13-5. Video i-f alignment by direct sweep and marker injection.

13-2-3. I-F Sweep Response Curve Analysis

Examples of i-f response curves are shown in Figs. 13-4 and 13-5. The frequency relation of the sound carrier to the picture carrier is reversed in the i-f amplifier (from that of the RF tuner) because the receiver local oscillator operates at a frequency higher than that of the transmitter carrier.

Note the following two characteristics of the picture i-f response curve: (1) the picture carrier is at approximately 40 or 50 per cent of maximum response; (2) the sound carrier must be at 1 per cent or less of maximum response. The picture carrier is placed at approximately 40 per cent of maximum response because of the nature of single side-band transmission, the system used in transmitting television signals. If the circuit is adjusted to put the picture carrier too high on the response curve, the effect will be a general decrease in picture quality caused by the resulting low-frequency attenuation; placing the picture carrier too low on the curve will cause loss of the low-frequency video response and result in poor definition. Loss of blanking and proper synchronization will also occur.

The skirt selectivity of the picture i-f curve is made sharp enough to reject the sound component of the composite signal. The sound carrier is kept at a low level to prevent interference with the video signal. To achieve this selectivity in split-sound receivers, an absorption circuit, consisting of a trap tuned to the sound intermediate frequency, is used. Some receivers include additional traps tuned to the higher frequency of the adjacent channel sound carrier. These traps have a marked effect on the shape of the response curve.

13-2-4. Alignment of Sound I-F Amplifiers and FM Detectors

The procedure used in aligning sound i-f amplifiers in both TV and FM receivers is similar. Intercarrier-type television receivers use a sound i-f of 4.5 MHz. Split-sound-type receivers may use either 21.25 MHz or 41.25 MHz. FM receivers use 10.7 MHz. Procedures for overall alignment of the sound section, including both the i-f amplifier and FM detector, may vary, depending upon the type of FM detector. The general procedures of Sec. 11-6 and Sec. 11-8 should apply to most television receivers.

13-2-5. Trap Alignment

One or more traps may be contained in the RF tuner and picture and sound i-f amplifiers, depending upon the type of television receiver. Traps are included to attenuate specific frequencies, such as adjacent picture and sound carriers, or picture and sound i-f signals in various parts of the receiver.

The test equipment setup for alignment of traps in various stages is essentially the same as for alignment of the particular stages (refer to Secs. 13-2-1–13-2-4). However, certain problems may be encountered.

Because the response of the amplifier is very low at the trap frequencies, the marker may often be difficult to see on the oscilloscope response curve. The use of marker adders is recommended for trap alignment. If extreme difficulty is encountered, the traps can be set with a d-c voltmeter rather than an oscilloscope. With such an arrangement, the d-c voltmeter is connected across the second detector load resistor, the marker generator is set for the trap frequency, and the trap is tuned for a minimum voltage reading on the meter.

The general procedure in aligning picture i-f amplifiers is first to set the traps, and then to align the amplifier circuits. Since any adjustment of the amplifier circuits will usually slightly detune the traps, the traps may have to be "touched up" during the picture i-f amplifier alignment. Again, the manufacturer's alignment instructions determine the exact procedure to follow.

Index